THE
VISION
PASSION
DISCIPLINE
& RISK OF A
NOBLE MAN

JAMES RYLE

PROMISE KEEPERS®
MEN OF INTEGRITY

Design and Typography: Exalt! Communications LLC

Printed in the United States of America
02 03 04 05 06/10 9 8 7 6 5 4 3 2 1

Contents

Introduction

"The noble man makes noble plans,
and by noble deeds he stands"

Isaiah 32:8, NIV

Men, this is a workbook. To get the best out of it, you must work it. Each week the reading material will take no more than 20 minutes to complete—making for a very short meeting, unless you do your part. If each of you will fully participate as a group as you work through this material, the Lord will use it to get the best out of you.

To experience the greatest success, follow these five guidelines:

1. Let one guy read the material out loud, while the others follow along. Switch off for variety.

2. Stop at the intervals provided in the narrative, and do what is suggested at each point.

3. Encourage each guy to participate in the discussions. Be intentional and patient.

4. Answer the questions in the Debriefing at the end of each week's lesson.

5. Pray for each other before you go home.

It is our prayer that the Spirit of Lord so move in your lives during the following weeks that each of you become a noble man in every sense of the word. A man of vision, passion, discipline, and risk—for the honor of Christ alone.

Climbing Companions

Before We Get Started...

Let's do a little mental gymnastics to get your brain in gear for this week's group discussion. Each guy take your best shot at completing this list of tongue twisters with the least amount of blunders. You know the rules; repeat each one three times as fast as you can. (No cheating by those who speak in tongues!) You've got 10 minutes...GO!

- She makes a proper cup of coffee in a copper coffee pot.

- Rubber baby buggy bumpers.

- The big black bug bled blue blood.

- Unique New York.

- Santa's Short Suit Shrunk.

- Weird rear wheels.

- Can Clarence cram a clam in a clean cream can?

- Eight great gray geese on green grass grazing.

- Red Buick, blue Buick.

- The great Greek grape growers grow great Greek grapes.

- He threw three free throws.

...wait, there's more!

A man once counseled his son that if he wanted to live a long life, the secret was to sprinkle a little gunpowder on his Cornflakes every morning. The son did this faithfully, and he lived to the age of 93. When he died, he left 14 children, 28 grand-children, 35 great-grandchildren, and a 15-foot hole in the wall of the crematorium!

OK, Now Let's Get Serious...

Climbing Companions

"When Jesus saw His ministry drawing huge crowds,
He climbed a hillside. Those who were apprenticed to Him,
the committed, climbed with Him.
Arriving at a quiet place, He sat down and taught
His climbing companions."

Matthew 5:1-2, THE MESSAGE

Crowds always collect around events and individuals that are curious or exciting. Jesus was all that and more, and so naturally His ministry drew large crowds. But He knew that crowds are fickle. So when He saw His ministry attracting large crowds—He climbed a hillside. This was a decisive movement upward; an intentional maneuver sure to root out those who were only looking for the easy way, the free ride. And as the Lord expected, the crowd dispersed. You see, crowds don't climb hillsides.

What happened next is what the Lord was after all along. Those who were apprenticed to Him—the committed— climbed with Him. Are you committed? When the crowds fade away, and following Jesus is no longer the popular thing to do—or the easy thing to do—will you be His climbing companion? If you will, He'll take you to the summit!

Big dreams create the magic that stirs men's souls to greatness.

Over the past several years Promise Keepers has hosted many events that have gathered literally hundreds of thousands of men in stadiums and arenas all across the nation. The crowds have surely gathered; and continue to do so even now.

But it is not about crowds. It's about climbing companions. It's about men who are committed to Christ, and to one another. It's about a brotherhood of guys from every ethnic group known to man, banding together to love, to learn, to live, and to leave a legacy. Men just like you. And, it's about time.

The Upward Call
The Scripture tells us that we are "partakers of a heavenly calling" (Hebrews 3:1). It is "the upward call of God in Christ Jesus" (Philippians 3:14). It is the call of God upon our lives that makes mediocrity unacceptable. The word mediocrity literally means "halfway up a mountain." Are you going to settle for only following Christ halfway? I didn't think so.

Jesus said, "I have come that you might have life, and have it more abundantly" (John 10:10). This means we are to live our lives above what is common. We are to be men of uncommon valor. We are to take the high road—even when others are lowdown, no good, and dirty. One old hymn says it so well...

I'm pressing on the upward way
New heights I'm gaining every day.
Still praying as I'm upward bound,
"Lord, plant my feet on higher ground."

My heart has no desire to stay
Where doubts arise and fears dismay.
Though some may dwell where these abound,
My prayer, my aim, is higher ground!

Lord lift me up! And let me stand
By faith on Heaven's stable land!
A higher place that I have found;
Lord, plant my feet on higher ground.

The Power of Brotherhood

"Big dreams create the magic that stirs men's souls to greatness." On a crisp September morning I heard Coach Bill McCartney say these words to a college football team—a team with a troubled past and an uncertain future. What happened next was almost magical. The team *believed* him.

And I watched as this group of young men bonded together as brothers, and dreamed themselves out of slumbering mediocrity into several seasons of sustained success. The year was 1989, the team was the Colorado Buffaloes, and the record of their turnaround and continued success stands to this day. They went from ashes to glory.

And now its your turn. By making this 12-week commitment to one another, you have started a journey together that will take you a long way toward becoming what you each hope in your heart you can be—a man of God. A climbing companion with the Son of God.

Over the next 12 weeks you will learn things about the Lord, yourself, and one another that will stir you to pursue excellence so that your life can bring honor to Jesus and make a difference in your sphere of influence. Indeed, this could be your championship season.

It Takes Teamwork to Make the Dream Work

If you will keep a heart of humility before the Lord and toward each other, being honest as you learn more about Jesus and about yourselves, this 12 weeks can launch you into a life of truly effective service for Christ.

It is certain that you cannot reach your greatest potential by yourself alone. Surely you know this to be true. No man is an island; our lives are inextricably designed by God to function only as we are vitally connected to Him—and to one another.

"Two are better than one," Solomon wrote, "because they have a good reward for their labor…and if one prevail against him, two shall withstand him; and a three-fold cord is not quickly broken" (Ecclesiastes 4:9-12). The Lord invites us to climb the hillside with Him, and as we do so we stand face to face with each other. Indeed—face to face; shoulder to shoulder; and, back to back.

As you faithfully meet together you provide an extraordinary power in one another's lives—the power of acceptance, affirmation, and accountability. These are three great needs every man has. And there are few things more powerful than when one man says to another, "I love you, I believe in you, and I am committed to you being everything God created you to be!" That's acceptance, affirmation, and accountability at its best. And that is what each of you bring to your group.

Never underestimate the importance of your part. And never hesitate to bring to the group that which the Lord has given you to say or to do—even if it seems insignificant.

Some men are decisive and out-going, ready at any moment to speak up and say what's on their heart. Others are quiet and reflective, and comfortable with sitting back while another leads the way. But if your group is to be as effective as possible, no one should say too much…or too little—each must do their part.

> The Lord invites us to climb the hillside with Him, and as we do so we stand face to face with each other.

Take a Minute…

Each week you will find the material in this workbook to be interactive. That is by design. It is our hope that this will help you as individuals, as well as a group, to become increasingly capable and empowered in formulating and expressing your views regarding Christ and His Word. In short, we intend to stir your heart with vision, passion, discipline, and risk so that you will dare to share your faith in an ever-increasing faithless world.

Take a minute and read the following Scriptures as our first step in that direction…

- 2 Timothy 1:6
- 1 Peter 4:10-11
- Romans 12:3-8
- 1 Corinthians 15:10
- Colossians 4:17
- 2 Timothy 4:5

Having read the previous Scriptures, write a brief summary of your thoughts regarding how these truths apply to your personal life.

_____

_____

_____

_____

_____

_____

_____

_____

In what way do you see this group helping you over the next 12 weeks?

_____

_____

_____

_____

_____

_____

_____

_____

Conclusion

Men, the surest way to have good success in your group is to establish and maintain an atmosphere of mutual trust and respect, giving each other the assurance of being accepted, affirmed, and held to the highest standard of accountability. It is not about control, it's about being conformed to the likeness of Christ—realizing that often the Lord is pleased to use those who know us best to challenge us most.

I have found the following declaration to be a good guiding principle for healthy relationships. I encourage you to read this out loud as a group, and then sign your name as a commitment to one another to practice this standard of honesty in your group:

> There is no question that cannot be asked.
>
> There is no issue that cannot be raised.
>
> There is no concern that cannot be expressed.
>
> There is no decision that cannot be challenged.
>
> And, together we will do the right thing.

_____

sign your name

Men, there is extraordinary potential in what you have just decided! If one can put a thousand to flight, and two ten thousand (Deuteronomy 32:30)—what on earth can God do through a group of guys like you?

Debriefing

1.   Describe how you sense God is calling you to higher ground.

2.   What does the phrase "man of God" mean to you?

3.   Each man take a moment and tell the others your earliest memories of having a best friend.

4.   Where do you hope to be as a man 12 weeks from now? As a group?

5.   How can the other guys pray for you right now?

WEEK TWO

The Gospel in a Single Sentence

Before We Get Started...

Just to make sure your brain is in gear while you sit on your rear, here is this week's dose of humor—having nothing whatsoever to do with the lesson. (For some of you guys this is the highlight of the week!)

On a guilt trip?

An elderly man in Italy had been secretly carrying a guilty conscience for several years. Unable to bear it any longer, he went to the local priest and said, "Father, I need to find peace over a private matter in my life."

"What is it, my son?" the priest responded. "Well," the old man said, "during World War II, I hid a refugee in my attic."

"That's nothing to be guilt-ridden over," the priest said. "What you did actually saved another person's life. Why, only God knows how great was the good that you have done. The devil is just trying to torment you for a good deed done to another."

"Yes, Father, I'm sure you're right," the old man replied, "but I charged him rent."

"Oh, I see," said the priest. "That clearly wasn't the best thing to do, but I'm sure the Lord has forgiven you after all these years."

"Well," the old man concluded, "then do you think I should tell the guy that the war is over?"

A Promise Keeper's Daily Prayer

"So far, God, I've done all right today. I haven't gossiped, I haven't lost my temper. I haven't been grumpy, nasty, or selfish. I haven't lied, cheated, or stolen anything from anybody. Nor have I yielded to temptations of lust, greed, pride, or ambition, and I'm really glad of that. But in a few minutes, Lord, I'm going to get out of bed; and from then on, I'll need a lot of help." AMEN

OK, Now Let's Get Serious...

9

The Gospel in a Single Sentence

"A certain nobleman went to a distant country
to receive a kingdom for himself, and then return."

Luke 19:12

There have been many great men and women throughout history, each shaping their world in ways that have lasted well beyond their time. In each and every one has been the indisputable presence of vision, passion, discipline, and risk.

There was no mountain too high, no valley too low, no ocean too wide, and no challenge too great to withstand the prevailing effects of vision, passion, discipline, and risk.

Of all the amazing figures who have passed through the Gates of Time into the Grand Hallway of human history, none is more singular and unsurpassed than Jesus of Nazareth, who is called Christ, the Son of the Living God.

Like all the others, Jesus was mission-focused. He said, "For the Son of man came to seek and to save that which was lost" (Luke 19:10). Everything about Him—His teaching, His miracles, and His death—*everything* served this one purpose.

> **W**hat is the "one thing" to which you bend all other considerations in your life? What would your friends say it is?

Dwight D. Eisenhower wrote, "We succeed in life as in war, only as we are able to identify a single, over-riding objective and then bend all other considerations to that one thing." May I ask, what is the "one thing" to which you bend all other considerations in your life? What would your friends say it is?

Jesus had a clear and compelling **vision**, evident even in His childhood. "I must be about My Father's business," he said at the young age of 12. His **passion**, ever ablaze in His sermons and always abundant in His miracles, carried Him all the way to the old rugged Cross. His **discipline**, which He cultivated in the dry depths of solitude and expressed in the floodtides of uncompromising devotion, sustained Him through the agony of death. And there, on a hill far away, He **risked** absolutely everything just to save you and me.

We Follow in His Steps

Vision, passion, discipline, and risk. As followers of Christ, these traits should become increasingly evident in our lives as we seek to make a difference in our world for Christ's sake. Jesus said to all who follow in His steps, "As the Father sent Me, even so send I you" (John 20:21).

Your life is a mission underway. Every day that you live, every breath that you take, every talent you have, every person you meet, everything that you do—all factor into the purpose God has for your life. You are an ambassador for Christ, a merchant of hope, a bringer of good news. And the Lord is with you everywhere you go.

His words, spoken from a mountainside so long ago, ring clear and true into every nook and cranny of our world today.

"All authority in heaven and on earth has been given to Me," Jesus said, "Therefore go and make disciples of all nations, baptizing them in the name of the Father and of the Son and of the Holy Spirit, and teaching them to obey everything I have commanded you. And surely I am with you always, to the very end of the age" (Matthew 28:18-20, NIV).

These are our standing orders, and we each must give account one day for the one life we have lived. Vision, passion, discipline, and risk are how that life is lived.

Vision produces passion as surely as a spark ignites a fire. Vision and passion produce discipline, for one whose heart is stirred by a noble cause will pay any price to see it realized. Vision, passion, and discipline provide the safest environment for one to take the greatest risks. And make no mistake about it—there is no way to live a fully effective Christian life apart from taking risks. The apostle Paul said it this way, "Anyone who wants to live all out for Christ is in for a lot of trouble; there is no way getting around it!" (2 Timothy 3:12, The Message).

Vision, passion, discipline, and risk—the benefits of having these qualities in your life will be enormous. Think about it—can you see how wonderful it would be to help your friends and loved ones find forgiveness of sin and a new life in Christ? Does your heart stir with a passion to do something that can help change the social climate of a nation by the power of the Gospel? Are you living within the guidelines of God's will for your life as an ambassador for Christ? And, will you take the risk associated with standing up and speaking the truth for Jesus Christ?

Vision, passion, discipline, and risk. It's what makes life worth living!

The Parable of the Talents
(Luke 19:12-27)

A certain nobleman went to a distant country to receive a kingdom for himself, and then return. And he called ten of his slaves, and gave them ten minas, and said to them, "Do business with this until I come back." But his citizens hated him, and sent a delegation after him, saying, "We do not want this man to reign over us."

And it came about that when he returned, after receiving the kingdom, he ordered that these slaves, to whom he had given the

money, be called to him in order that he might know what business they had done.

And the first appeared, saying, "Master, your mina has made ten minas more." And he said to him, "Well done, good slave, because you have been faithful in a very little thing, be in authority over ten cities."

And the second came, saying, "Your mina, master, has made five minas." And he said to him also, "And you are to be over five cities."

And another came, saying, "Master, behold your mina, which I kept put away in a handkerchief; for I was afraid of you, because you are an exacting man; you take up what you did not lay down, and reap what you did not sow."

> Does your heart stir with a passion to do something that can help change the social climate of a nation by the power of the Gospel?

He said to him, "By your own words I will judge you, you worthless slave. Did you know that I am an exacting man, taking up what I did not lay down, and reaping what I did not sow? Then why did you not put the money in the bank, and having come, I would have collected it with interest?"

And he said to the bystanders, "Take the mina away from him, and give it to the one who has the ten minas." And they said to him, "Master, he has ten minas already." I tell you, that to everyone who has shall more be given, but from the one who does not have, even what he does have shall be taken away.

But these enemies of mine, who did not want me to reign over them, bring them here and slay them in my presence.

Men, this single story will serve as the biblical foundation for our discussion together over the next several weeks. I encourage you to read it every day until it becomes so familiar to you that you could literally quote it from memory. Trust me, it will become one of your favorite stories ever told by Jesus.

So, let's begin by looking at how Jesus summed up the Gospel in a single sentence.

The Gospel in a Single Sentence

Jesus began the story by presenting the Gospel in a single sentence—"A certain nobleman went to a distant country to receive a kingdom for himself, and then return." This sentence touches on several foundational truths of the Christian faith. Let me explain.

The word **"certain"** means "unique and distinct", as in "only begotten Son." There has never been, nor will there ever be any other man like Jesus of Nazareth. He was born of a virgin, without sin in any way. This is certain.

The Bible says, "God so loved the world He gave His only begotten Son, that whosoever believes in Him should not perish, but have everlasting life." Jesus is God's only Son. Therefore, Jesus is man's only Savior. As one preacher said, "Christ is not one of many ways to God, nor is he the best of several ways. He is the only way."

Jesus Himself said, "I am the way, the truth, and the life; no man comes to the Father but by Me." Christ is the way unchanging; He is the truth infallible; He is the life everlasting. Jesus is the way that you might be saved. He is the truth that you might be sure. He is the life that you might be satisfied.

Far from being narrow and unfair, this is the most generous and fairest of all possible solutions. God did not leave us to ourselves to find a way back to Him, for who among us knows where God is that we could first find Him for ourselves, and then chart the path for all others to follow?

God alone knows where He is. God alone knows where we are. And God alone knows what it takes for us to return to Him. The Bible says that God "longs for all to be saved and to understand this truth: that God is on one side and all the people on the other side, and Christ Jesus, himself man, is between them to bring them together, by giving his life for all mankind" (1 Timothy 2:4-6, Living Bible).

The word **"nobleman"** speaks of the sinless life this certain man lived among us. He was tempted in all points like us, yet without sin. Never once—in thought, word, or deed—did Jesus ever sin. This uniquely qualifies Him to be the perfect sacrifice for sinners. Having no sins of His own to die for, His death on the cross now covers all of our sins!

His death, burial, resurrection, and ascension into heaven are all included in the words **"went to a distant country"**—for that is how the Nobleman passed from this earth into Heaven.

Jesus said, "I go to prepare a place for you." He is there in heaven even now doing just that. And while there He "ever lives to make intercession" (Hebrews 7:25). In other words, He loves to pray for you as He sits at His Father's right hand. Let me ask you, when was the last time you asked Jesus to pray for you? Why not ask Him now!

The Nobleman went to a far country **"to receive a kingdom for himself."** This is clearly referring to the exaltation of Jesus Christ as Lord. For "God has given Him a name that is above every name, that at the name of Jesus every knee shall bow and every tongue confess that Jesus Christ is Lord to the glory of God the Father" (Philippians 2:9-11).

And, last but not least, the phrase "**and then return**" assures us of the hope of all ages—the Second Coming of Christ!

The Gospel in a single sentence—"A certain nobleman went to a distant country to receive a kingdom for himself, and then return." Men, commit this sentence to memory and use it as a mental outline for sharing your faith with your friends and family members.

Here, in the simplest of words, is the Gospel that we preach. Jesus was born without sin, and He lived without sinning. When He died on the cross, having no sins of His own to pay for, He paid the price for our sins. He was buried, and on the third day God raised Him from the dead—since death had no rightful claim upon a sinless man.

He was then taken into heaven and declared to be the Lord of all, the evidence of which is the Holy Spirit poured forth in our world establishing the influence of Christ's Kingdom in the hearts and lives of men and women from every tribe and nation.

God alone knows where He is. God alone knows where we are. And God alone knows what it takes for us to return to Him.

One day, at a time known only to God, Christ will return to this earth and abolish sin and death by creating a new heaven and a new earth, filled with the glory of God.

That's it. So simple even a child can understand it. Those who believe this and turn from their sins, trusting Christ for salvation, will be born again by the Spirit of God and brought into God's purpose for their lives here on earth.

Vision, passion, discipline, and risk will become the characteristics of each life that follows Jesus and seeks to maximize the talents God has given them to use during their time in this world. And then, by death or by rapture, enter into the joy of the Lord.

Where Will Your Name be Written?

The RMS Titanic, the ill-fated luxury liner, had a passenger list of some of the world's richest and most influential people. She was supposedly unsinkable, yet went down in the icy waters of the North Atlantic on her maiden voyage in the early morning of April 15, 1912. Over 1,500 perished at sea; there were fewer than half as many survivors. At shore the names were posted in two simple and unmistakable columns—SAVED and LOST.

This planet Earth, a Great Titan on its maiden voyage among the stars of God's heaven, is itself on a collision course with a great and dreadful Day of Judgment. Though many scoff at the thought, the unthinkable will happen—the unsinkable

will sink. And on that final Day when the names are posted on the shores of glory, we will not be listed according to our wealth, status, fame, achievements, religious affiliation or ethnicity.

No. There will be but two columns of names recorded in august and sobering finality—SAVED and LOST. On which list, my friend, will your name appear?

Debriefing

1. Tell of the day you trusted Christ as your Savior and Lord. How did it happen? What has your life been like since that day?

2. What is the "one thing" to which you bend all other considerations in your life? What would your friends say it is?

3. What are some things that hold you back from sharing your faith with others?

4. Take a match, light it, and before its burns out—that's how much time you have to lead a lost man to Christ. Can you do it?

5. Jesus came to seek and to save the lost. Make a list of five individuals you are asking Christ to save, and are willing for Him to use you to reach them:

- _____

- _____

- _____

- _____

- _____

DISCIPLINE

Prayer

Father in heaven,

Thank you for loving me, and for sending Jesus to seek and to save me. Jesus, thank you for being faithful to your vision, for being passionate and disciplined in your obedience, and for risking it all on my behalf.

Holy Spirit, take my life and let it be a true and effective witness for Christ. Use me to bring honor to God by being a blessing to others; especially to these five individuals I have listed. Give me the joy of seeing each one come to Christ before the Lord returns!

AMEN.

The Call of the King

Before We Get Started…

Two good ol' boys went to the local junkyard to rummage for car parts. The owner told them to go out back and find what they needed, and then he would work out a price with them.

"You boys watch out for my dog," he told them. "He's out there to keep thieves from breaking in at night, so he shouldn't bother you. But just in case, keep your eyes opened."

The two went cautiously into the yard, more than a little concerned about running into the old man's dog. Slowly working their way around, they came upon an old abandoned well.

"How deep do you think it is?" one said to the other. "I don't know," he replied, "let's throws a brick down it and see how long it takes to hit the bottom." They never heard it hit.

Seeing an old car battery nearby they threw it down the well, thinking a heavier object would be easier to hear. Still no sound. "Hey, let's throw this old engine block down the well," one said., "it's so heavy we're bound to hear it hit bottom."

As soon as they dropped the engine, the junk yard dog came racing from around an old wreck. His teeth were glistening in the sun, his growl sounded like a crazed lion, his eyes were blood red with rage, and white foam was streaming from both sides of his mouth. He jumped right at the two men. Fortunately for them the dog missed and fell down in the well.

The old man, hearing all the racket, came out of the shop and asked, "Are you boys alright?" "Yes sir, " they answered.

"My dog didn't bite you, did he? I heard him barking. Is everything OK?"

"Well, sir," the men replied, "we don't know how to tell you this…but your dog just jumped down the well."

The old man stared in disbelief, and then said, "No, that's not possible. I had him chained up to an old engine block."

OK, Now let's get serious…

The Call of the King

"He called ten of His servants."

Luke 19:13

Have you ever been in a place where the phone kept ringing and nobody answered it? In moments like that it seems everybody is busy with something else, assuming that somebody else will answer the call. But nobody does. After awhile it can get to be quite annoying. There is something irritating about an incessant, unanswered call.

Over the years I have noticed a similar thing in the lives of many men—a call that is not being answered. A call from God. Busy with so many other things, and sure that the call is for someone else, many men lose themselves in trivial moments and miss the momentous opportunity to answer the call of God on their lives. Have you answered the call?

Missing out on God's call for your life would be the worst thing that could happen. Research shows that one of the greatest fears men face is having lived a meaningless life; a life that didn't matter; a life that made no difference. This dreadful thought haunts even the most accomplished of individuals. Maybe it haunts you even now.

Os Guinness wrote, "Our passion is to know that we are fulfilling the purpose for which we are on earth. All other standards of success—wealth, power, position, knowledge, and friendships—all grow tiny and hollow if we do not satisfy this deeper longing."

> Busy with so many other things, and sure that the call is for someone else, many men lose themselves in trivial moments and miss the momentous opportunity to answer the call of God on their lives.

Each of us longs to know that our lives counted; that we accomplished what we were put on this earth to do. Yet, in an odd contradiction, nothing is more common than unrealized potential. Most of us settle for far less than we are capable of being, and of doing.

On the one hand we want our lives to count; on the other hand, we seem far too willing to become marginalized into mediocrity. Our only hope is to answer the call of God upon our lives.

Vision, Passion, Discipline, and Risk

Abraham traveling into the unknown, Joseph remaining faithful in Egypt, Moses crossing the Red Sea, Joshua conquering the Promised Land, David slaying a giant and becoming a king, Isaiah telling his visions, Zechariah telling his dreams, Daniel in the Lion's den, Nehemiah rebuilding the walls, Zerubbabel rebuilding the temple, Simon Peter leaving his fishing nets, Paul preaching the Gospel, John writing the Revelation—each one of these ordinary men heard and answered the call of God, and as a result lived extraordinary lives.

Vision, passion, discipline, and risk—these are the marks of a noble brotherhood assembled by the Son of God down through the ages; men called out of mediocrity into magnificence; followers of Jesus from each generation who have left their world better than they found it.

They each heard God's voice and followed Him with trusting hearts—marked by vision, passion, discipline, and risk. And now it's your turn.

The Lord longs for you to answer the call and be a part of this timeless team. And in your heart as a man, you know it's what you want to do more than anything else in the world!

Take a Moment...

Read the following Scriptures regarding *the Call of God*, and discuss your thoughts as a group.

- 1 Corinthians 1:26
- Ephesians 1:18
- 2 Peter 1:10
- Philippians 3:14
- 2 Thessalonians 1:11

In the Parable of the Talents, Jesus said that the Nobleman "called ten of His servants." We know Jesus is talking about Himself, and our relationship to His call upon each of our lives. He has called us into His service, and entrusted us with the resources necessary to fulfill the call. The only question that remains is: Have we answered the call?

RISK

A Man Named Peter

"Follow Me," Jesus said, "and I will make you a fisher of men" (Matthew 4:19). This is how Simon Peter's journey with Jesus began—he was given a vision of being something other than what he was.

Christ saw him not simply as he was, but as he would be. And Jesus committed Himself to making Peter everything he had the potential of becoming. But Peter had to answer the call. And so do you.

Peter could have said no. He could have stayed with the nets and the boat and the fish, and followed in the traditions of his father. He could have remained in Capernaum, his hometown, and lived out his days in anonymous mediocrity. And so can you.

> He has called us into His service, and entrusted us with the resources necessary to fulfill the call. The only question that remains is: Have we answered the Call?

But Peter said yes! And as a result, he not only walked on water—he walked into history! He became a cherished hero to millions of Christ-followers throughout history, who see in Peter so much of themselves.

Jesus gave him vision, and this produced a passion that marked Peter throughout his life. His eagerness to impress Jesus, his moodiness when rebuked, his crazy zeal in vowing to be faithful when others fell away—all these and more stem from his deep, abiding passion for Christ.

The Lord added to Peter's vision and passion the necessary ingredient of discipline—otherwise Peter would not have gone the distance. He responded to the process of being disciplined, and was therefore not only willing, but able, to take remarkable risks as a faithful follower of Jesus.

And as Joe White has said, "Peter left his nets, stepped out of the boat, and followed Jesus all the way to the cross." Vision, passion, discipline, and risk. That's how Peter did it.

And now, men, it's our turn. As it was for Jesus, and for Peter—so it is for us. Vision, passion, discipline, and risk. These are the keys.

Let's Get Practical

Let's look at a practical way to hear and answer God's call on your life. These five steps will help you.

Step # 1—Desire

The Bible says, "For God is working in you, giving you the desire to obey him and the power to do what pleases him" (Philippians 2:13, NIV).

Realizing that God is stirring your heart to desire to do His will, what do you want to do with your life? What are your deepest and most cherished hopes and dreams? What would be a worthy use of the one life you have been given? The Bible says, "He will give you the desires of your heart."

The first step on this wondrous journey is desire; what do you really, *really* want to do with your life? Go around the circle right now and have each guy answer that question out loud.

Step # 2—Ability

What are you actually able to do? God not only makes you willing to obey Him, but also makes you able; He gives you the skill to do His will. Simon Peter was given not only the desire to bring people to Jesus, he was also given the ability.

Take a moment and discuss with each other in the group what you feel your abilities are—and equally important—what you feel you are not able to do. Encourage one another in this process.

One guy may not see his abilities as clearly as his friends do, so it's important that they build him up with encouragement. On the other hand, another guy may see himself as more able than he actually is, and thereby set himself up for serious disappointment. Be a friend and help him see the truth…in a loving way.

Step # 3—Opportunity

Does the opportunity to do what you desire seem to naturally present itself? Maybe you have the desire and the ability to do something in particular, but the opportunity to do it never comes.

Have you found that some doors just won't open up to you as you pursue your dreams? Maybe this is God's way of redirecting your life back to His better choice for you.

The Lord opens doors that no man can close, and closes doors that no man can open. Our problem is that we camp with regret at the door that has closed, and miss the door that has opened!

If you desire to do something but find that the opportunity to do it is just not coming to you, maybe God is saving you for something better—something He desires for you.

And, if you desire and are doing what God has called you to do, the opportunities will be there in abundance. Whatever God has called you to do, and enabled you to do, He will also provide the opportunities for you to do it.

Maybe you are indeed on the right path, and yet the doors of opportunity are still not opening. Perhaps the timing of the Lord is not yet, and so you haven't been given the opportunity to do what you desire and are able to do.

Wait on the Lord, and seize the opportunity provided by this down time to prepare yourself so that when the door opens—you will be ready!

Step # 4—Results

What happens to others when you do this thing you desire? What happens to *you* when you do what you feel is God's will for your life? If nothing happens, maybe you are not doing what God wants you to do.

Jesus said, "You know a tree by its fruit" (Matthew 7:16-20). Fruit is another word for results. It is the produce of your life and labor. What fruit is your life producing? Good fruit, or bitter fruit? When you do God's will in God's way the fruit your life produces is sweet and lasting.

> **W**hat do you want to do with your life? What are your deepest and most cherished hopes and dreams? What would be a worthy use of the one life you have been given? The Bible says, "He will give you the desires of your heart."

OK, so what have we learned? First there is the desire, and then there is the ability. Then there is the opportunity followed by good results. These steps chart the path of answering God's call on your life. Which brings us to the last step.

Step # 5—Perseverance

How far can you go in life doing this thing? Paul said, "I have fought a good fight, I have finished my course, I have kept the faith" (2 Timothy 4:7, NIV). One translation puts it this way, "I have run the full distance." Can you go the distance in this thing you desire to do with your life? Or, will something else along the way divert your affections and aspirations, turning you aside to other pursuits?

Jesus said, "I have finished the work You gave Me to do" (John 17:4, NIV). There are many who start well enough, but few who finish strong. When you take the path that God has chosen for your life you will have what it takes to go the distance and finish well.

Conclusion

Kierkegaard, the Danish philosopher, told a story about a goose who was wounded and landed in a barnyard with some chickens. He played with the chickens and ate with the chickens. After a while, that goose thought he was a chicken.

One day a gaggle of geese flew overhead, migrating home. They gave a honk up in the sky, and the barnyard goose heard it.

Kierkegaard said, "Something stirred within the breast of this goose. Something called him to the skies. He began to flap the wings he hadn't used, and he rose a few feet into the air. Then he stopped, and he settled back again into the mud of the barnyard. He heard the upward call, but he settled for less."

Friend, the phone is ringing. God is calling you. Nobody can answer this call but you. The longer you wait before answering, the more annoying your life be-

comes to those around you. There are few things as disruptive to the peace of other people's lives than a person who is running from God. How many lives are being distressed because you won't answer the call?

Hey, buddy, pick up the phone!

Debriefing

1. How can a man recognize that God is calling him?

2. Describe to each other what you sense God is calling you to do.

3. What are some of the things that keep you from freely and fully answering God's call on your life?

4. How can the other guys pray for you?

During this coming week, each time you hear a phone ring let it serve as a reminder that you have answered God's call on your life.
And reaffirm it with a short, quiet prayer—
"Thank You Lord for calling me, and for helping me answer the call."

You Got the Goods

Before We Get Started...

In our ongoing effort to help a man become a vital part of his local church, we offer the following:

10 Ways to Survive Dull Sermons

1. Pass a note to the worship leader asking whether he or she plays requests.
2. Move to as many different seats as possible, without being too obvious.
3. Raise your hand and ask for permission to go to the bathroom.
4. Scratch your arm and shoulder and see how many other people you can make itch.
5. Stare at the preacher with your eyes wide open.
6. See if a yawn really is contagious.
7. Slap your neighbor and see if they turn the other cheek. If not, raise your hand and tell the usher.
8. Signal to the minister that his fly is undone.
9. Draw your arms up into your sleeves and turn your shirt around backwards.
10. Start from the back of the church and try to crawl all the way to the front, under the pews, without being noticed.

...wait, there's more!

Gandhi walked barefoot most of the time, which produced unusually thick calluses on his feet. He also ate very little, which made him rather frail. And his odd diet caused him to suffer from bad breath. Altogether this made him—(brace yourself guys, this is a groaner)—A super callused fragile mystic hexed by halitosis.

OK, Now Let's Get Serious...

You Got the Goods

"(He) delivered unto them his goods."

Matthew 25:14

Few things are more frustrating to a man than to be faced with a task and not be given the time, the training, or the tools to get the job done. Few situations are more likely to produce this frustration in a man than the general state of affairs in contemporary church life.

While the sermons are theologically sound, verbally astute, and passionately presented—more often than not they end up being completely useless. At least when it comes to actually training and equipping men to really make a difference in their daily world.

After all is said and done, there's a lot more said than is done. The pastor preaches a stirring series on Prayer, but no one prays—except the faithful few who were already praying. The pastor preaches about Reconciliation, but no one makes any intentional, long-lasting commitment to reach across racial boundaries and build meaningful friendships with people of differing ethnicity.

> It seems we know what to say, and how to say it—but for all our talk there doesn't seem to be any real or lasting changes.

The pastor lays out a series of sermons about Leading the Lost to Christ, but one year later the church is the same as before—no one is being saved. And always there is the annual sermon about Giving—and the people give for awhile, but then fade back into old habits. Until about a year later, and the sermon comes out once again.

And so on and so on and so on.

What's a Guy to Do?

It seems we know what to say, and how to say it—but for all our talk there doesn't seem to be any real or lasting changes. Amidst the bells and smells, the songs and sermons—many guys sit in church scratching their heads, wondering how to tell their lost boss about Jesus without getting fired. Or how to suggest to their friends that they lighten up on the racial jokes. Or how to win the private battles of sexual temptation. Or how to do an honest day's work for an honest day's pay.

Feeling spiritually untrained and personally ill-equipped, most of us struggle with basic day to day challenges. Fat chance then, that we are going to jump in line to "go into all the world and preach the Gospel to every creature." And we feel more and more guilty each time someone brings the topic up. Like right now.

Have I Got Good News for You!

The disciples said to Jesus, "Lord, teach us to pray." And Jesus did so. On another occasion Jesus said to His disciples, "Follow Me, and I will make you fishers of men." They followed, and Jesus delivered on His promise. These two occasions show us that the desire to be taught the things of the Spirit is strong in the heart of godly men, and Jesus is more than accommodating.

Furthermore, Jesus doesn't just train us, He also *entrusts* us with the resources to get the job done. As the Scripture says, "(He) delivered unto them his goods."

How strange it must have been for a fisherman named Simon Peter to be called by an itinerant rabbi named Jesus, to follow Him and become a "fisher of men." In his later years Peter wrote, "His divine power has given unto us all things that pertain to life and godliness" (2 Peter 1:3, NIV). He was writing from personal experience. Jesus called him, trained him, trusted him, and entrusted him with the high privilege of presenting the Gospel to ordinary men and women with extraordinary results— thousands were saved!

Peter had no idea that first day he met Jesus just how radically different his life would become in a few short years. The same is true of you. Your life matters to God far more than you may realize. And by placing it fully in His hands, trusting Him to keep you in step with His Spirit, you can do whatever the Lord has called you to do—for He has also given you everything you need to get the job done. You got the goods!

What are the Goods He has given Us?

Rather than open the cargo doors and unload each specific package given by Jesus to every individual that He has called unto Himself, it will better serve our purpose to look at the bigger picture. With this in mind, there are at least six ways that the Lord has seen to it that we have all we need to do everything He has called us to do.

#1—The Holy Spirit

Jesus never made a promise that He failed to keep. He said, "You shall receive power after the Holy Spirit is come upon you, and you shall be My witnesses...unto the uttermost parts of the world" (Acts 1:8).

Peter, filled with the Holy Spirit on the day of Pentecost, said, "the promise is unto you, and to your children, and to all that are afar off, even as many as the Lord our God shall call" (Acts 2:39). This means you and me!

Imagine it, men—the very same Spirit that raised Christ from the dead has been made to dwell in you. The same Holy Spirit that fell upon the first disciples at Pentecost, empowering them to stand publicly and boldly for Jesus Christ, is now here for you! They were ordinary men—just like you and me—but the awesome power of God's Holy Spirit enabled them to do extraordinary things. And that power is at work in you even now, lifting you upward and pressing you onward to please the Lord in all things! You got the goods!

> **Your life matters to God far more than you may realize.**

#2—The Bible

We have a more sure word from God in the Bible than in any other source of inspiration that exists. William Cowper wrote, "A glory gilds the sacred page, majestic like the sun; It gives a light to every age, it gives, but borrows none."

The word *Bible* comes from a Greek term meaning "many books." Our Bible is in fact a library; a collection of 66 books bound together in one remarkable volume.

- These books were written by at least 40 authors, from five continents, over a period of about 1,500 years.
- The authors come from a wide range of personality and occupation. There are prophets, shepherds, fishermen, kings, peasants, explorers, builders, soldiers, scribes, theologians, poets, and priests. Yet, despite the enormous diversity of its writers—the Bible has a unity of subject, structure, and spirit unparalleled in all of literature.
- It contains a consistent system of doctrinal and moral utterances that positively effect individuals, as well as nations.
- Its unique treatment of certain themes—such as the holy, the true, the good, and the future—are equally mysterious, authoritative, and practical.
- The Bible is the most widely translated and circulated book in the world. This is an even more amazing fact when you take into account that its early translators were killed, and many of its early readers were imprisoned.
- The Bible, as we know it today, has been in existence for almost 19 centuries but it is always relevant to the day. Its quotations and its motifs are found in our literature, oratory, art, music, politics, law, and ethics. Its influence is inescapable.

Charles Spurgeon said, "A Bible that's falling apart usually belongs to a man who is not!" Men, you have been given the Bible. It is as vital to your soul as food and water are to your body.

Dwight L. Moody said, "Sin will keep you from this Book; this Book will keep you from sin." And, one more quote worth your attention: "All things desirable to men are contained in the Bible" (Abraham Lincoln).

Hey guys, you got the goods!

#3—The Church

"It is not good that man be alone." This was not simply an observation God made; it was a *declaration*. He created us to be part of a society. The problem is that sin has caused society to fall into such divisions and distortions that it no longer provides what God intended.

So He created a *new* society—the Church! Your participation in this society causes you to grow in ways you never will apart from it. It helps you discover and develop the many wonderful gifts God has given you to serve Him better.

Someone once said, "If the only tool you have is a hammer, you tend to see every problem as a nail." That's true. And that's why you need to be part of a larger circle of friends so you can appreciate all the other tools that are out there. Now the guy next to you may not be the sharpest tool in the shed, but he is in the shed—and that's the point! And that's also why Jesus calls you to active involvement in His Church. You got the goods!

#4—Spiritual Gifts

Peter, a man who clearly knew the grace of God in a very personal way, left us this counsel— "As each man has received the gift, even so minister the same to one another as stewards of the manifold grace of God" (1 Peter 4:10).

You have been given a unique cluster of spiritual gifts and natural abilities that make your participation in God's purposes vital. Simply said, it is unacceptable that you opt out for any other thing. Your gifts matter to God—and to the rest of us! When you don't show up with what God gave you, the rest of us suffer setbacks in our own service. And even your own soul suffers—not only here, but also when you stand before the Lord one day. "Whatever portion of your gifts you siphon off to the world," Bill Hybels said, "will be your regret in heaven."

Hey, guys, let's aim high! How about showing up together in heaven with no regrets!

You got the goods!

#5—Life Experiences

"All things work together for good to those who love God and are called according to His purpose" (Romans 8:28). Joseph knew this to be true long ago in Egypt. He said to his brothers, "You meant it for evil, but God meant it for good" (Genesis 50:20).

The great need each man faces is to see his life experiences from Jesus' point of view. "Everything makes us bitter or better," I once heard John Wimber say. He was right. Think of how your experiences in life have shaped you. Every event has contributed in a meaningful way to your ultimate effectiveness as an ambassador for Jesus Christ.

When we walk with Jesus through our life experiences, He brings out the best in us—not the worst. And this makes us merchants of hope in an otherwise hopeless world. You got the goods!

#6—Opportunities

Inasmuch as God has given you the desire and the ability to do His will, and has supported you with meaningful friends who encourage you in your journey—and seeing He has gifted you in unique ways with natural and spiritual gifts, and shaped your life with experiences that have prepared you for such a time as this—doesn't it just make sense that He would also give you every opportunity to maximize your life's potential?

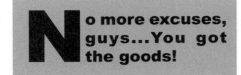

No more excuses, guys...You got the goods!

Whatever God has called you to do; you can be assured that He will give you plenty of opportunities to do it. But don't look off in the distance for some great and future thing to come your way—life's greatest opportunities come to those who make the most of small ones today. "Now is the watchword of the wise" (C.H. Spurgeon).

When the Lord gives you the opportunity to share your faith with a lost friend—do it right then; you got the goods! When the Lord provides you an opportunity to advance the cause of racial reconciliation in our world—do it right then! Any time you have the chance to do good to another for the honor of Christ—do it!

No more excuses, guys...You got the goods!

Debriefing

1. In light of the fact that the Lord has given us His goods, take a few minutes and tell how your life has been positively impacted by:

    *   The Holy Spirit
    *   The Bible
    *   The Church
    *   Spiritual Gifts
    *   Life Experiences
    *   Opportunities

2. If you could change one thing about your present relationship with Jesus, what would it be? And why would you change it?

3. How can the guys pray for you this week?

Doing the King's Business

Before We Get Started...

A pig walked into a convenience store and asked, "Do you serve root beer?" The storekeeper said he did. "I'd like one, please," said the pig. When the pig was done he asked to use the rest room. While the pig was in the restroom, another pig came in and asked for two root beers. When he was done he asked for the rest room, just like the first pig. While he was in the restroom, two more pigs came in. One pig ordered three root beers, and the other pig ordered four. When they were done, they both needed to use the rest room.

And while they were in the restroom, a fifth pig came in. At this point the storekeeper spoke up. "Let me guess," he said, "you want five root beers." The fifth pig was amazed. "Why, yes, " he answered, "Yes, I would like five root beers."

He drank each one and when he was done, the fifth pig turned to walk out of the store. At this point the storekeeper was bewildered. "Don't you want to use the rest room like the other four pigs?" he asked. "Of course not," the pig answered, "I'm the fifth little piggy—I go wee-wee-wee all the way home."

...wait, there's more!

Five passengers shared a plane ride through the Rockies. A scientist, a politician, a minister, a college student, and the pilot. When the engine stalled the pilot said, "Sorry, we've only got four parachutes. I must take one because my large family needs me." With that he grabbed a parachute and jumped.

The politician said, "The country needs me now more than ever," and he too jumped. Then the scientist said, "I'm the smartest man alive; the world cannot afford to lose me." So he grabbed another pack and jumped.

The minister turned to the student and said, "I've lived a full and meaningful life. I'm ready to meet my Maker. You take the last chute and go." The student calmly replied, "Oh I don't think that's necessary, Pastor. You see, the smartest man in the world just jumped out of the plane with my backpack!"

OK, Now Let's Get Serious...

Doing the King's Business

"Do business with this until I return."

Luke 19:13

At the young age of 12 Jesus said, "I must be about My Father's business" (Luke 2:49). What were you doing when you were 12? What are you doing now? Let me ask it this way, "What *must* you do with your life?" Sooner or later we each must be able to answer that question with clarity and conviction. The sooner the better.

I once heard an economist say, "Unemployment is a characteristic unique to the human species only. All other creatures and created things seem to know what they are supposed to be doing—and are doing it." Do you know what you're supposed to be doing? Are you doing it?

General William Booth, founder of the Salvation Army, was asked the secret of his amazing Christian life. Booth answered, "I told the Lord that he could have all that there is of William Booth." God took that one life, filled it with vision, passion, discipline, and risk—and our world is a better

> Unemployment is a characteristic unique to the human species only. All other creatures and created things seem to know what they are supposed to be doing—and are doing it.

place because of it. What on earth could happen if you were to fully give your life to Christ? And He were to fill it with vision, passion, discipline, and risk? What army might you lead for Christ!?

John Wesley wrote, "The Possessor of heaven and earth placed you here, not as a proprietor, but as a steward." Men, the King has entrusted you with His goods, and now He trusts you to use them to do His business. The question we must answer is, What is the King's business?

The King's Business

The Scriptures leave us with no doubt as to how Jesus spent His days. "Jesus went about doing good," the Bible says, "healing all who were oppressed by the devil; for God was with Him" (Acts 10:38).

Take a few moments and read the following Bible verses, listing beside each one the principle activity described in the verse. In other words, read the verse and answer this question: What did Jesus do?

- Luke 4:18 _____

- Luke 19:10 _____

- 1 John 3:8 _____

- John 10:10 _____

- 2 Corinthians 5:18 _____

Your list should show that Jesus came to preach the Gospel in a way that went beyond words. He came to seek and to save that which was lost; destroying the power of the devil, and giving life abundantly to all who trust Him. Now He has committed unto us the ministry of reconciliation, that we may do for others as He has done for us. That's the King's business.

If you will do the King's business, then your life—with all its talents, abilities, resources, experiences, and opportunities—is to be about the business of *preaching the Gospel.*

Now don't let that throw you for a loop. It doesn't mean that you have to be a preacher behind a pulpit. "Preach the Gospel at all times," St. Francis said, "and if necessary use words."

Often our actions speak louder than our words—and that is where the real Gospel meets the real world. Jesus preached the Gospel, and backed up what He said by works of compassion, healing, and social empowerment.

If you will do the King's business, then your life—with all its talents, abilities, resources, experiences, and opportunities—is to be about the business of *seeking and saving that which is lost.*

The first part is to seek them out, which requires us to go to where they are. The second part is to save, which requires us to walk them all the way to Jesus—who alone can save.

RISK

If you will do the King's business, then your life—with all its talents, abilities, resources, experiences, and opportunities—is to be about the business of *destroying the works of the devil*.

Make no mistake about it, there is evil in this world and it must be destroyed. Dr. Martin Luther King, Jr. said, "Injustice anywhere is a threat to justice everywhere." Another has said, "All that is necessary for evil to triumph is for good men to do nothing."

God has called us to be men of faith and action; the two are inseparable. As the body without the spirit is dead, so faith without action is dead. "Cowardice asks, 'Is it safe?' Consensus asks, 'Is it popular?' and Conscience asks, 'Is it right?'" (Dr. King).

Vision, passion, discipline, and risk—when given by God and directed by His Spirit—will always do the right thing, even if it's unsafe and unpopular.

> **V**ision, passion, discipline, and risk—when given by God and directed by His Spirit—will always do the right thing, even if it's unsafe and unpopular.

If you will do the King's business, then your life—with all its talents, abilities, resources, experiences, and opportunities—is to be about the business of *helping others experience abundant life*.

All men are created equal and endowed by their Creator with certain inalienable rights; among them are life, liberty, and the pursuit of happiness. None should be deprived of these things, except those who act in wickedness to deprive others of them.

Inequality is ungodly. There are no signs of discrimination, or class preference in heaven. There the streets are gold and have no names, and all citizens walk equally in the presence of the Lord.

Jesus taught us to pray, "Thy kingdom come…Thy will be done on earth as it is in heaven." God longs for all to be saved and come to the knowledge of the truth. He wants all to experience the freedom that Jesus gives. He lifts up the broken-hearted, and cares for the oppressed. He has called us into His business of doing the same.

If you will do the King's business, then your life—with all its talents, abilities, resources, experiences, and opportunities—is to be about the business of *reconciliation*.

Racial divisions and cultural strife are not God's will. Just as Joseph, the favored son of Jacob, was decked with the famed coat of many colors, so Jesus, the only begotten Son of God, is clothed with Royal robes that encompass all the nationalities of Adam's ransomed race. And they are already singing in heaven.

St. John the Beloved saw with his own eyes, and heard with his own ears that sweet melody of a reconciled society— "And they sung a new song, saying, thou art worthy to take the book, and to open the seals thereof: for thou wast slain, and hast redeemed us to God by thy blood out of every kindred, and tongue, and people, and nation" (Revelation 5:9). O to God that Earth would soon echo that Heavenly anthem!

The Most Dangerous Prayer You Could Pray

Several years ago I heard an old preacher enthusiastically and cautiously offer the congregation a dangerous prayer. He suggested that before we pray it, we ought to carefully consider the full implications of doing so. Now all these years later, I'm the old preacher—and he was right! I offer this prayer to you with the same enthusiasm and caution. Here it is:

> "Dear Lord Jesus, do in me
> *anything* You need to do,
> so You can do through me
> *everything* You want to do."
> AMEN

If there is any doubt in your mind about whether or not you want the Lord to actually answer this prayer—then under no circumstances should you ever even think to pray it! For the truth is He will always answer this prayer—even during those times when you may wish you had never prayed it!

And, I guess I should go ahead and tell you that the very fact you even read the words may already have been taken by the Lord as you actually praying the prayer—so it's probably too late for you to get out of it. Sorry. Welcome to the major leagues.

In all seriousness, the Lord is deliberate in answering a prayer like this because He has something in mind; something great He is wanting to accomplish not only in our lives, but through our lives for others. Men, say yes to Jesus and begin to live life at its best and fullest—marked by vision, passion, discipline, and risk.

In the Parable of the Talents, Jesus tells us that the Nobleman (Himself), called His servants (that's us), and delivered unto them His goods. He then said, "Do business with this until I return."

Obviously Jesus has not yet returned, so we are clearly in the midst of this unfolding story. All that remains to be seen is which of the story's characters we are, which role we end up playing in life.

Will we be the faithful servants who hear Him say, "Well done!" Or will we be the wicked servant who lived in fear and slothfulness, only to be rebuked when the Lord returned? Worse yet, will we be numbered among those who reject Christ altogether, and so perish in their sins?

This is a weighty thing.

Conclusion

"A zealous man is pre-eminently a man of one thing. It is not enough to say that he is earnest, hearty, uncompromising, thorough-going, whole-hearted, fervent in spirit. He only sees one thing, he cares for one thing, he lives for one thing, he is swallowed up in one thing; and that one thing is to please God. Whether he lives, or whether he dies; whether he is rich, or whether he is poor; whether he pleases man, or whether he gives offense; whether he is thought wise, or whether he is thought foolish; whether he gets blame, or whether he gets praise; whether he gets honor, or whether he gets shame— for all this the zealous man cares nothing at all. He bums for one thing; and that one thing is to please God, and to advance God's glory" (J.C. Ryle, 1816-1900).

> Will we be the faithful servants who hear Him say, "Well done!" Or will we be the wicked servant who lived in fear and slothfulness, only to be rebuked when the Lord returned?

Brothers, let's please God by doing the King's business!

Debriefing

1. What would you say is the one thing your life *must* accomplish?

2. What are you determined to do this next week that reflects your commit-ment to "do the King's business"? Write it down.

_____

_____

_____

_____

_____

_____

_____

_____

_____

_____

3. How can the others in this group pray for you?

WEEK SIX

Trouble in River City

Before We Get Started...

OK guys, by now you know the routine...here are a few more choice nuggets that will give you something to pass on to the guys you work with. (Perhaps it would also be nice if you pass along some of this other stuff you're learning, too! It's just a thought.)

Things that Make You Go "Hmmmm"
- Change is inevitable...except from vending machines.
- Borrow money from pessimists—they don't expect it back.
- If at first you don't succeed, skydiving is not for you.
- Money can't buy happiness. But it sure makes misery easier to live with.
- For every action, there is an equal and opposite criticism.
- The sooner you fall behind, the more time you'll have to catch up.
- Time wounds all heels.
- Statistics show that one out of every four Americans is suffering from some form of mental illness. Think of your three best friends. If they are okay, then it's you.
- Deja Moo: The feeling that you've heard this bull before.

...wait, there's more!

Did you hear about the guy who wasn't paying attention to where he was going and ran right through a screen door?

He strained himself.

OK, Now Let's Get Serious...

Trouble in River City

"But his citizens hated him, and sent a message after him, saying,
'We will not have this man to reign over us.'"

Luke 19:14

A nobleman of impeccable character, grand generosity, expanding estate, and international renown. A man among men, who exemplifies in the finest sense of every word the enormous potential of vision, passion, discipline, and risk.

The story seems almost too good to be true. Thankfully it does not begin with "Once upon a time," or we never would have believed it. Rather, it starts with a simple though sweeping declaration, "A certain nobleman went into a far country to receive for himself a kingdom, and to return."

The Gospel in a single sentence.

The story opens with such promise, but the plot quickly darkens as we soon learn that all is not well. "His citizens hated him," the text reads, "and they sent a message after him saying, 'We will not have this man to reign over us!'"

In other words, there is trouble in River City.

> It is the devil's chief design to have men blame God for things that happen in the course of life that don't seem fair, or right, or good.

It has always intrigued me that his citizens hated him. Hated him so much in fact that they sent notice while he was away that they had no intention of submitting to his rule upon his return. What did he do to upset them so? What was the justification for their insolence and revolt?

The truth is there was no justification for their hatred. Nor did he do anything that merited their rebellious disdain. A sinister force had been at work spreading slanderous lies about the King, and using these lies to stir the hearts of ignorant men to perform acts of eternal stupidity.

Of course I am speaking of Christ and His kingdom, and the work of Satan in perverting the minds of fallen men so as to have them reject Christ altogether, and thus enter into a Christless eternity doomed forever.

It is the devil's chief design to have men blame God for things that happen in the course of life that don't seem fair, or right, or good. A child is killed by a crazed predator, or dies of some dreadful disease—and God gets blamed. Someone's life savings are lost in an economic collapse—and God gets blamed. Our favorite sports team loses the championship game—and God gets blamed. And on it goes from the awful to the absurd…covering all points in between.

Such is the case in this story of the Nobleman. He who is good gets blamed for the bad.

Who Do Men Say that I Am?

Ask any self-righteous Pharisee and he would quickly tell you that Jesus was a blasphemer, a false prophet, a raving madman, a drunkard, a glutton, or a demon-possessed fraud.

Ask those who are less important in their own eyes and they will suggest that Jesus was a political revolutionary, a magician, a peasant unwittingly caught up in social revolution, a charismatic prophet foretelling the end of the world, a "marginal" Jew who challenged the teachings and practices of the religious leaders of his day, or a spiritual master who overcame the humblest of origins to proclaim the Gospel of love and forgiveness.

Ask Simon Peter, and millions of others just like him, and they will tell you that Jesus is the Christ, Son of the Living God.

But none of that ultimately matters as far as you are concerned. The simple and sobering fact is you must answer for yourself the inescapable question of the ages, asked by Jesus Himself to every soul who has ever, or will ever live— "Who do *you* say that I am?"

As a group take a moment and let each guy answer this question. And here's a tip: instead of trying to be correct with your answer—just be honest. That's the only way God would have it, for it provides our only chance for growth.

Jesus Christ is Lord

"Jesus Christ is Lord!" God alone knows exactly how many of our forefathers spoke these enduring words of truth at the price of their lives. History is replete with legendary accounts of humble, yet noble, men and women who were burned at the stake, beheaded, thrown to wild beasts, and in other ways tortured for their devotion to Jesus Christ.

What is this power that moves men and women to not count their own lives dear unto themselves that they may confess before the world their faith in Christ as Lord.

PASSION

Rulers scoffed at such blind faith and then raged in fury against such true allegiance for another. Unable to strike Christ Himself, they turned their swords against those who follow Him in love. But, as one has said, "He has walked by the graveside of earth's fallen kings who opposed Him and yet He still reigneth."

Take a Minute...

Read the following Scriptures; in fact, guys, it would be a great benefit to your spirit to commit these verses to memory. I know it looks like a tall order, but you can do it; and you'll be glad you did:

- Luke 2:11
- John 13:13
- John 20:28
- Acts 2:36
- Acts 10:36
- Romans 10:9-12
- Romans 14:9
- Philippians 2:11

> The American Dream is about having as much education, strength, and money as we can possibly acquire. The pursuit of these things often determine the lives we end up living...or losing.

"Jesus Christ is Lord!" This was the Church's earliest confession, and it will be the rally cry of the faithful who hold firm to the end. It has been, and remains, the abiding test of authentic Christianity. So, how do you measure up? Is Jesus Christ Lord of your life?

Do You Know the Lord?

Among the many things that dominate our deepest dreams as men, there are three that stand out above the rest. No, they are not sex, sex, and sex. Rather, they are Knowledge, Strength, and Wealth.

Think about how much of who you are in the eyes of others (and perhaps even yourself) is defined by your level of intelligence, your physical appearance and abilities, and your bank account. Indeed, the American Dream is about having as much education, strength, and money as we can possibly acquire. The pursuit of these things often determines the lives we end up living...or losing.

The Lord used Jeremiah the prophet to deliver a timeless truth for men of all ages. "Let not the wise man boast of his wisdom, or the strong man boast of his strength or the rich man boast of his riches," Jeremiah wrote, "but let him who boasts boast about this: that he understands and knows me, that I am the LORD, who exercises kindness, justice and righteousness on earth, for in these I delight" (Jeremiah 9:23-24, NIV).

So you're smart with many degrees, and have keen insight into many different fields of knowledge—but, do you know the Lord? And, my, aren't you a physical specimen, strong and resilient, looking as though you've just come down from Olympus—but, do you know the Lord? And, when it comes to money, you are loaded, with no end in sight of all the riches you are yet to acquire—but, do you know the Lord?

Jesus asked, "Who do men say that I am?" And then, driving the point home to the heart of every man, He asked, "Who do *you* say that I am?" Friend, do you know the Lord?

In the Parable of the Talents the citizens did not know Him, and so they hated Him out of pride and ignorance. The last servant did not know Him, and so was afraid of Him. The faithful servants *did* know the Lord, and so they loved Him, and served Him faithfully. Which one are you?

The Name and Fame of Jesus

The Bible says, "There is salvation in no other, for there is none other name under heaven given among men whereby we must be saved" (Acts 4:12). There is only one name that opens heaven's doors and God's heart—the name of Jesus. There is only one name that breaks the power of sin and sets the captive free—the name of Jesus. There is only one name worthy of all praise, and deserving of your allegiance—the name of Jesus.

Early on in His public ministry the name and fame of Jesus spread like a prairie fire on a windy day. People all throughout the region—rich and poor, king and commoner, Jew and Gentile—all heard of Him; for His fame was ever-increasing.

His death on the cross did not have the effect the rulers of the day had hoped. He rose from the dead and His followers became invincible in their faith—so much in fact that in ever-widening circles the number of disciples increased vastly in Jerusalem; and many of the Jewish priests were themselves converted as well.

Paul the apostle, a few years later wrote, "Finally, dear brothers, as I come to the end of this letter, I ask you to pray for us. Pray first that the Lord's message will spread rapidly and triumph wherever it goes, winning converts everywhere as it did when it came to you" (2 Thessalonians 3:1, Living Bible).

Jesus Christ! He is peerless in His exaltation, unrivaled in His Lordship, incomparable in His grace, invincible in His power, unassisted in His work as Redeemer, matchless in His mercy, adored in His glory and worshipped in the beauty of His holiness. In His birth is our significance. In His life is our example. In His death is our forgiveness. In His resurrection is our hope. In His Second Coming is our consummate glory!

Isaiah spoke for us all when he said, "LORD, Your name and renown are the desire of our hearts" (Isaiah 28:8, NIV). Men, we live in a fallen world where hostilities toward God run high and hot. For this reason we must become men of vision, passion, discipline, and risk—laying ourselves out for the high honor of one Name alone...Jesus.

Conclusion

While citizens hate the Lord, and cowards fear Him, we who are His servants must excel in our love for Him. The truth is—our authentic faith and bright conduct as happy servants of the King may be the only hope others have of ever recovering from the deception of Satan and the ruin of sin. Our faithfulness in dark moments of history may be the only light that some will ever see. "Let your light so shine before men that they may see your good works, and glorify your Father in heaven" (Matthew 5:16).

Peter exhorted us to "sanctify the Lord God in your hearts: and be ready always to give an answer to every man that asks you a reason of the hope that is in you" (1 Peter 3:15). Do you know the Lord? If so, then you can make Him known!

Daniel said, "the people who do know their God shall be strong and do exploits" (Daniel 11:32). Dr. King said, "The ultimate measure of a man is not where he stands in moments of comfort and convenience, but where he stands at times of challenge and controversy." Men who take action in the face of passivity and perversion fill God's heart with pleasure, and transform their world with power—the power of love.

> **Men who take action in the face of passivity and perversion fill God's heart with pleasure, and transform their world with power—the power of love.**

Paul the apostle was described by James, the Lord's brother, as a man who "hazarded his life for the name of our Lord Jesus Christ" (Acts 15:26). What an epitaph! Could the same be said of you? Wouldn't you want it to be? The word "hazarded" literally means "to hand over." Have you handed your life over to the Lord Jesus Christ?

Paul summed up his own life story in a single sentence when he stood before a king who held in his hand the power of life and death. "O Agrippa," he affirmed, "I was not disobedient unto the heavenly vision!" (Acts 26:19). Vision, passion, discipline, and risk. It is what marks every true man of God.

It is the desperate need of the hour.

Debriefing

1. Describe a time when you felt like blaming God for something that went wrong or bad. How did the Lord bring you through that to a place of faith and trust again?

2. How would you go about explaining Christ's Lordship to someone who is lost, or who believes that there are many ways to get to God besides Jesus Christ.

3. What would it look like for you to "hand your life over" to Jesus completely?

4. In what ways would others say that you have brought fame to the Name of Jesus?

5. How can the other guys here pray for you right now?

DISCIPLINE

PROMISE KEEPERS
MEN OF INTEGRITY

A Day of Reckoning

Before We Get Started...

There was a logger in Oregon who was out of work because of the controversy surrounding an endangered species—the white spotted owl. The woods where the loggers had been working was now declared a natural reserve for this one bird. You can imagine the stir that was created when this logger, Willy, was arrested for shooting one of the owls.

The press, ever ready to make a national story out of anything, demanded swift justice for this murderous beast of a man. The judge, a childhood friend of Willy, was in a real bind. When Willy was brought before him he said, "Willy, I can't believe you would be so stupid as to go and shoot one of them blasted birds. You know I'm gonna have to throw the book at you!"

"Yes, your honor," Willy respectfully replied, "But, first could I tell you why I shot it?" The judge agreed. And Willy told his tale. "Your honor, I've been out of work for a few months now, and the only way I can feed my family is by hunting. I was in the woods looking for game—and the only thing I could find was that owl. I didn't shoot it to break the law; I just needed to feed my kids."

With that the judge shifted in his chair and said, "This may change things for you. I'm sure once the press hears the rest of the story they will understand if we let you off with just a fine or something. But, before I call them in here," the judge continued, "I'm curious to know—just what does a white spotted owl taste like?"

"Oh," Willy answered, sealing his fate, "it tastes kind of like a cross between a California condor and an American bald eagle."

But wait, there's more...

A personal notice in the local paper read: "Lost dog. One eye, three legs, one ear bitten off, recently neutered. Answers to the name, Lucky."

OK, Now Let's Get Serious...

A Day of Reckoning

"And it came to pass that He returned."

Luke 19:15

A day of reckoning is coming. A day in which the Books will be opened, and the dead—both small and great—will stand before God and be judged out of those things which were written in the books, according to their works (Revelation 20:12). The Lord is coming back, and when He comes it will seem quite abrupt, like a thief in the night. Thousands of years may span the time between when Christ was first here and when He comes again—but it will all seem as the fading of a light mist on a hot summer day when Gabriel blows his legendary horn.

One day, sooner than you realize, you will stand before the Lord to give account of this one life you have lived.

A day of reckoning is coming. One day, sooner than you realize, you will stand before the Lord to give account of this one life you have lived. Indeed, the Bible clearly teaches that each one of us must give account of himself to God. I will not have to answer to God for you, and you will not have to answer to God for me. Each man will stand and answer for himself alone. How vital it is, therefore, that we be noble men of vision, passion, discipline, and risk.

A Short Bible Study

Guys, take a minute and read the following Scriptures. Then discuss with one another the implications of these truths for your life in today's temporary world.

- Matthew 10:15
- Matthew 12:36
- John 5:28-29
- Acts 24:24-25
- Romans 14:10-12
- 2 Corinthians 5:9-10
- Hebrews 9:27

The Bible says, "And it came to pass, that when he returned, having received the kingdom, then he commanded these servants to be called unto him, to whom he had given the money, that he might know how much every man had gained by trading" (Luke 19:15).

Mark recorded the story this way, "For the Son of man is as a man taking a far journey, who left his house, and gave authority to his servants, and to every man his work, and commanded the porter to watch. Watch ye therefore: for ye know not when the master of the house cometh, at even, or at midnight, or at the cockcrowing, or in the morning: Lest coming suddenly he find you sleeping. And what I say unto you I say unto all, Watch" (Mark 13:34-37).

Matthew Henry commented about this passage, "Our Lord Jesus, when he ascended on high, left something for all his servants to do. We ought to be always upon our watch, in expectation of his return. This applies to Christ's coming to us at our death, as well as to the general judgment. We know not whether our Master will come in the days of youth, or middle age, or old age; but, as soon as we are born, we begin to die, and therefore we must expect death. Our great care must be, that, whenever our Lord comes, he may not find us secure, indulging in ease and sloth, mindless of our work and duty. He says to all, Watch, that you may be found in peace, without spot, and blameless."

In the parable of the talents, Jesus tells us that the Nobleman returned and called his servants to give an account of what they had done with that which He had entrusted unto them. We will examine their responses in the next two lessons. For now, let's focus on the more pressing issue of our personal need to be ready for that Day when the Lord returns.

It was said of Martin Luther that his calendar had but two days: Today, and That Day. He lived each day in light of the final Day. We would do well to follow his example.

The Finality of Unbelief

The story of the talents, as told by Jesus, has some very sobering truths presented in it, not the least of which is when He said, "Bring here those enemies of mine, who did not want me to reign over them, and slay them before me" (Luke 19:27, NKJV).

There is a finality to unbelief. Those who reject Christ and refuse God's only provision for salvation will most surely die in their sins. The Bible leaves nothing vague on this matter, for the stakes are high and eternal. The writer of the book of Hebrews presents the clearest case regarding this weighty issue:

RISK

Anyone who disobeys the Law of Moses is put to death without any mercy when judged guilty from the evidence of two or more witnesses. What, then, of those who despise the Son of God? who treat as a cheap thing the blood of God's covenant which purified them from sin? who insult the Spirit of grace?

Just think how much worse is the punishment they will deserve! For we know who said, "I will take revenge, I will repay"; and who also said, "The Lord will judge his people." It is a terrifying thing to fall into the hands of the living God! (Hebrews 10:28-31, Good News Bible).

Moreover, Jesus said, "Whosoever shall fall on this stone shall be broken: but on whomsoever it shall fall, it will grind him to powder" (Matthew 21:44). Christ is the Rock. You and I must fall upon Him and be broken—redeemed from all self-righteousness and sinful independence. Otherwise, the Rock will fall on us and we will be crushed—separated forever from God, and from all things good and holy.

C.S. Lewis wrote, "In the end there will be two categories of people. Those who say to God, 'Thy will be done,' and thus enter Heaven; and those to whom God says, 'Thy will be done,' as they enter Hell."

> Christ is the Rock. You and I must fall upon Him and be broken—redeemed from all self-righteousness and sinful independence. Otherwise, the Rock will fall on us and we will be crushed—separated forever from God, and from all things good and holy.

A Day of Reckoning is coming for believer and unbeliever alike. For those who reject Christ it will be a day of terror—and finality. For those who love the Lord, and served Him faithfully in life, it will be a day of reward and great joy. We will discuss this more in detail in the following weeks, but for now let's look at what we can do to be best prepared for that coming Day.

A Hope that is Eternal

We have been justified by faith, and have peace with God through Jesus Christ. We now stand in grace and rejoice in hope of the glory of God. But as Paul contended, "If in this life only we have hope in Christ, we are of all men most miserable" (1 Corinthians 15:19). Christ has risen from the dead and thereby given us full assurance of our hope. Now our lives can be everything God intends while we are on this earth, and our future in heaven holds only the brightest of possibilities. Our hope is eternal!

John the Beloved put it this way, " Beloved, now are we the sons of God, and it doth not yet appear what we shall be: but we know that, when he shall appear, we shall be like him; for we shall see him as he is." He then added, "And every man that hath this hope in him purifieth himself, even as he is pure" (1 John 3:2-3).

Our hope of Christ's return, and of eternal blessing in Heaven, should have a clear and comprehensive influence in our lives while we live on this earth. The Lord is coming back, and will call you and me to answer for our time here on earth. How then shall we live to be best prepared for that Day?

We Should Live With...

- **Vigilance—Matthew 24:44**

Read the Scripture, then give an example of how vigilance could be more evident in your life.

_____

_____

_____

_____

- **Moderation—Philippians 4:5**

Read the Scripture, then give an example of how moderation could be more evident in your life.

_____

_____

_____

_____

- **Patience—James 5:8**

Read the Scripture, then give an example of how patience could be more evident in your life.

_____

_____

_____

_____

- **Stewardship—Luke 19:13**

Read the Scripture, then give an example of how stewardship could be more evident in your life.

_____

_____

_____

_____

PROMISE
KEEPERS®
MEN OF INTEGRITY

- **Dependence—1 John 2:28**

Read the Scripture, then give an example of how dependence upon Jesus could be more evident in your life.

_____

_____

_____

_____

_____

- **Faithfulness—1 Timothy 6:14**

Read the Scripture, then give an example of how faithfulness to God's Word could be more evident in your life.

_____

_____

_____

_____

_____

- **Holiness—1 Thessalonians 5:23**

Read the Scripture, then give an example of how holiness could be more evident in your life.

> Our lives can be everything God intends while we are on this earth, and our future in heaven holds only the brightest of possibilities. Our hope is eternal!

_____

_____

_____

_____

_____

- **Resolve—Revelation 3:11**

Read the Scripture, then give an example of how resolve could be more evident in your life.

_____

_____

_____

_____

_____

Conclusion

"According to the grace of God which was given to me, as a wise master builder I have laid the foundation, and another builds on it. But let each one take

heed how he builds on it. For no other foundation can anyone lay than that which is laid, which is Jesus Christ. Now if anyone builds on this foundation *with* gold, silver, precious stones, wood, hay, straw, each one's work will become clear; for the Day will declare it, because it will be revealed by fire; and the fire will test each one's work, of what sort it is. If anyone's work which he has built on *it* endures, he will receive a reward. If anyone's work is burned, he will suffer loss; but he himself will be saved, yet so as through fire" (1 Corinthians 3:10-15, NKJV).

Debriefing

1. Describe how you are feeling having finished this lesson.

2. How will this affect your attitude toward your unsaved friends and relatives?

3. What would help you share your faith more effectively?

4. Are you ready to stand before the Lord?

5. How can the other guys in this group pray for you right now?

The Man Who Delivers the Goods

Before We Get Started...

You're Drinking Way too Much Coffee if...

1. Your eyes stay open when you sneeze.
2. The only time you're standing still is during an earthquake.
3. You can jump-start your car without cables.
4. You go to AA meetings just for the free coffee.
5. You can take a picture of yourself from ten feet away without using the timer.
6. You're so wired, you pick up FM radio.
7. Instant coffee takes too long.
8. You want to be cremated just so you can spend the rest of eternity in a coffee can.
9. Your lips are permanently stuck in the sipping position.
10. You introduce your wife as your "Coffeemate."

...wait, there's more!

One summer day a bird flew over a park where a huge family picnic was being held. He decided to stop for a while and to help himself to some of the food. He especially went after the stack of baloney sandwiches on one end of the large table. The family wasn't paying much attention, being preoccupied with fun and games, so the bird ate to his heart's content. However, he found he was so full that he could not get off the ground. Fortunately there was a long rake leaning against the end of the table, and the bloated bird was able to climb up to the tip of the rake handle. From there he tried to launch himself into flight. Alas, his weight was so great that he fell solidly to the ground and died. The moral of this story is: Never fly off the handle when you are full of baloney!

OK, Now Let's Get Serious...

The boy Samuel prophesying at the Tabernacle of Shiloh.

The Man Who Delivers the Goods

"Well done, good servant!"

Luke 19:17

The boy Samuel prophesying at the Tabernacle of Shiloh. Young Samson fighting the lion at Timnath. The youthful David slaying the giant Goliath in the valley of the Philistines. Young Solomon ascending the throne of Israel. The boy Jesus confounding the lawyers in the Temple of Jerusalem. *Every* boy dreams of that defining moment in his own life when he becomes a man—a man whose life counts; a man who makes a difference; a man who delivers the goods.

> There is a man in this world who is never turned down,
> Wherever he chances to stray.
> He gets the glad hand in the populace town,
> Or out where the farmers make hay.
> He is greeted with pleasure on hot desert sands,
> Or deep in the aisles of the woods.
> Wherever he goes, there's a welcoming hand—
> He's the man who delivers the goods!
> Walt Whitman

In the Parable of the Talents Jesus draws our attention to three particular servants. Each had been given the same amount and charged with the same directive, "Do business with this until I return."

Upon His return an accounting was to be given. Each of the three servants came and reported how they had done with what the Nobleman had entrusted unto them. The first servant said, "You gave me one, and it has made ten more!" The second servant reported, "The one you gave me has made five more." And the third servant said, "You gave me one and I buried it. Here, you can have it back."

In this week's study we will look at the two men who were faithful and delivered the goods. Next week we will look at the guy who called it quits.

> Every boy dreams of that defining moment in his own life when he becomes a man—a man whose life counts; a man who makes a difference; a man who delivers the goods.

But before we go any further, let's clear up a potential problem. Luke tells us that Jesus gave each servant one pound apiece. But Matthew records that one servant was given 5 pounds, another was given 2 pounds, and the third was given one pound (Matthew 25:14-26). Furthermore, the man with five, gained five more by trading; and the man with two, gained two more. Why the discrepancy in the numbers?

Opportunities and Abilities

The difference between the two accounts has to do with the specific purpose of each one. Luke is writing to show that we each have been given the same *opportunity* to use our one life in an effective way for the cause of Christ and His Gospel. Matthew specifically tells us that the talents were given "to each according to his ability."

In other words, though we all have equal *opportunity*—we each have been given differing measures of *abilities* with which we can serve the Lord uniquely, as well as effectively. Let's take a minute and look closer at each one of these.

Opportunities

The Bible teaches that God appointed each one of us to live at a specific time in history, and in a specific place on earth (Acts 17:26). He also appointed us a specific task to accomplish with our lives (Acts 22:10). After our lives are done, it has been appointed unto us to die and then face the Lord in judgment (Hebrews 9:27). We even have an appointment to sit with the Lord at His table in heaven after the judgment passes (Luke 22:29)!

Hey guys, most of you keep some kind of an appointment book to manage your time. Make sure these appointments are entered into the ledger!

Abilities

While we all have the same opportunity to honor the Lord with our lives, He has uniquely fashioned each one of us with differing abilities and talents. The Bible says that each man has been dealt a measure of faith (Romans 12:3), and that we each have been given a measure of grace (Ephesians 4:7). Paul said, "I will not boast beyond the measure God has assigned to me" (2 Corinthians 10:13). Do you know what your measure is?

The man next to you may have more faith than you; you may have more grace than him. But both of you have exactly what you need to live your life so as to bring the greatest honor to Jesus. You have a measure that suits you perfectly, and for which you must give account one day to God.

Faithfulness

While Luke and Matthew differ in their accounts of what was given to the servants, both make it clear that the principle issue is our being faithful with what the Lord has given to us. Faithful with the opportunities He has given us to tell others of His love and power, and faithful with the talents and abilities He has given us to bring honor to His name.

So, guys, the question is—are you being faithful? Are you being faithful with the opportunity the Lord has given you to serve Him while you live on this earth? And are you being faithful with the many gifts, abilities, and talents He has entrusted to your stewardship? It is a haunting question, I know, but it must be answered. For one day we each will stand before the Lord and give account for the one life we lived—why not take time on this day to give thought to how we are going to fare in that day?

> So, guys, the question is—are you being faithful? Are you being faithful with the opportunity the Lord has given you to serve Him while you live on this Earth?

What Was Their Secret?

There must've been considerable risk in the venture these servants undertook for their Lord—certainly so in the case of the one who increased his talent from one to ten. Such a high return on a single investment requires great risk, tenacious watchfulness, market savvy, and sheer guts. No doubt he spent many sleepless nights in prayer, and many long days filled with uncertainty as to the outcome of his labors. And, oh, what joy when his faith paid off and his labors were rewarded! What a prize he had to show his Lord when He returned!

"Look!" he said with great excitement, "You gave me one pound, and it has yielded ten!" And the Nobleman replied, "Well done, good and faithful servant!" A happy day indeed.

The same may be said for the servant who took his one talent and increased it to five. Though he gained only half as much as the other, he no doubt gave the same 100% of his faith and efforts. And his joy was equally great.

What was their secret? How did these two servants pull off their service for Christ with such success? The answer is simple. In both cases each servant did fully what they had faith to do; and, that faith expressed itself in vision, passion, discipline, and risk. "But the bravest are surely those who have the clearest vision of what is before them, glory and danger alike, and yet notwithstanding go out to meet it" (Thucydides, 460-400 BC).

The Bible says, "Faith without works is dead." Anybody can talk a good game, but sooner or later you gotta put your money where your mouth is and take it to the field. Jesus said, "Why call Me Lord, and do not the things which I say?" Those who talk, but do not *do*—have no vision, no passion, are without discipline, and take no risk.

But such was not the case for these two faithful servants in the parable. They had vision—vision of an investment with high returns. That alone would motivate any enterprising soul, but these guys had something even more motivating. They longed for the day when they would hear those most cherished of words, "Well done, thou good and faithful servant." That was the vision that drove them onward. It guided each decision they made, each risk they took.

Their vision produced a passion in their souls that energized them to go the distance, to reach for their dream. Because they never lost sight of where they were going they could put up with anything along the way. They followed the example of Jesus, who "for the joy that was set before Him endured the cross." When your eye is on the prize, the base and profane do not hold sway over your soul. Godly passion says no to lesser things for the hope of seeing a great thing come to pass.

Men, what great thing stirs your imagination with such hope that you happily forsake the lure of lesser things? The hymnist put it best, "I am resolved no longer to linger charmed by the world's delights. Things that are nobler, things that are higher; these have allured my sights!"

Discipline is required to pursue with passion a vision that is noble. Whatever your vision may be—however great it is—you will never see it realized without discipline. Bill McCartney once told his football team, "Greatness comes through the discipline of attending to the details." Discipline creates an undaunting faithfulness to stay the course through thick or thin—and ultimately to win the prize. These two faithful servants embraced the discipline required to work tirelessly and wait for the good results of their daring labors.

Take a Risk

Vision produces passion. Vision and passion produce discipline. Vision, passion, and discipline provide the safest environment for you to take the greatest risks. Risk is opportunity fully embraced, with the chance of failure looming large on the horizon.

What if I'm wrong? What if it doesn't work out? What if I lose everything? These questions face every hearty soul that dares to step out in faith and take a stand for Jesus in today's world.

The status quo requires no risk. Nothing ventured; nothing gained. But excellence, by its very nature, requires that you break out of the pack and pull away from the common and ordinary, shaking off the mundane and mediocre. Hey, the only thing in the middle of the road is yellow stripes and dead armadillos!

John Maxwell has said on many occasions, "If you always do what you've always done, you'll always get what you've always got." So, guys, if you want something that you've never had you must do something that you've never done. And that is where *risk* comes into the equation.

- Noah built a boat in the middle of a desert—that was a risk.

- Abraham left his home and went out, not knowing where he was going—that was a risk.

- Moses forsook the security of Pharaoh's palace, choosing rather to suffer affliction with the people of God—that was a risk.

- Daniel prayed to God though the king had decreed death to any who dared do so—that was a risk.

- David faced a giant in the open field of battle—that was a risk.

- John the Baptist confronted the sins of King Herod—that was a risk.

- Peter walked on water—that was a risk.

- Paul openly declared to Caesar himself that Jesus Christ is Lord—that was a risk.

> The status quo requires no risk. Nothing ventured; nothing gained. But excellence, by its very nature, requires that you break out of the pack and pull away from the common and ordinary, shaking off the mundane and mediocre.

These were men of whom the world was not worthy. These are the fathers of our faith, and we are their sons. Now it is our turn. Now we have the opportunity and the abilities to not only follow in their steps, but to go beyond where they themselves were able to go. But it will require a definite dose of vision, passion, discipline, and risk.

Rudyard Kipling wrote an excellent poem, called *If—*, that stirs the hearts of noble men who want to make a difference in this world with their lives. Perhaps he was talking to you…

If you can keep your head when all about you
   Are losing theirs and blaming it on you;
If you can trust yourself when all men doubt you,
   But make allowance for their doubting too;
If you can wait and not be tired by waiting,
   Or, being lied about, don't deal in lies,
Or, being hated, don't give way to hating,
   And yet don't look too good, nor talk too wise:

If you can dream—and not make dreams your master;
   If you can think—and not make thoughts your aim;
If you can meet with Triumph and Disaster
   And treat those two imposters just the same;
If you can bear to hear the truth you've spoken
   Twisted by knaves to make a trap for fools,
Or watch the things you gave your life to broken,
   And stoop and build them up with worn out tools:

If you can make one heap of all your winnings
   And risk it on one turn of pitch-and-toss,
And lose, and start again at your beginnings
   And never breathe a word about your loss;
If you can force your heart and nerve and sinew
   To serve your turn long after they are gone,
And so hold on when there is nothing in you
   Except the Will which says to them: "Hold on"

If you can talk with crowds and keep your virtue,
   Or walk with Kings—nor lose the common touch;
If neither foes nor loving friends can hurt you;
   If all men count with you, but none too much;
If you can fill the unforgiving minute
   With sixty seconds' worth of distance run—
Yours is the Earth and everything that's in it,
   And—which is more—you'll be a Man, my son!

Indeed—you'll be a man who delivers the goods!

DISCIPLINE

Debriefing

1. In what way could it be said of you that you "delivered the goods?"

2. What is the most risky thing you've ever done for Christ?

3. What part of Kipling's poem hits you where you live?

4. How can the other guys here pray for you right now?

WEEK NINE

The Guy Who Called it Quits

Before We Get Started...

Once again guys we come to that time where we stop for a moment of levity, not forsaking the limits of brevity. A merry heart does the soul good like medicine—so here's a dose to cheer you up.

A General and his chief aide, a handsome young Lieutenant, were traveling across the U.S. on a civilian train. Sharing their compartment was a lovely young lady and her elderly grandmother. At one point during the trip the train entered a long dark tunnel. Everyone was silent as the train sped through the darkness. Then two distinct sounds were heard. The first was a long kiss, and the second was a loud slap.

When the train exited the tunnel into daylight, the four passengers each had a different explanation of what had just occurred.

The young lady thought, "How forward of that handsome young Lieutenant to kiss me, but why would my grandmother slap him?"

The grandmother thought, "How dare that young man kiss my granddaughter; but how proud I am that she slapped him!"

The General thought, "That was a bold move the young Lieutenant made in kissing that lovely young lady, but why did she slap me?"

The Lieutenant thought, "What a day! What a day! I not only kiss a lovely young lady, but also slap my General and get away with it!"

Wait...there's more!

It was a fine sunny day as two young skunks were scurrying about in the woods, mindless and carefree. Suddenly, one skunk turned and said to the other, "My instincts tell me it's going to rain." The other skunk paused, as though deep in thought, and then replied. "That's funny," he said, "My end stinks and it don't tell me nothing!"

OK, Now Let's Get Serious...

The Guy Who Called it Quits

"I was afraid of you."

Luke 19:17

The summer sun was unseasonably hot. The strength and conditioning coach, nicknamed "Mad Dog" by the players, seemed unreasonably intense as he pushed harder and harder upon those trying out for the football team during two-a-days in August 1990. The college football world was buzzing with the University of Colorado's golden season the year before, and now everybody wanted on the bandwagon.

There were two guys in particular who showed up supposing they could make it as walk-ons. They were flabby and undisciplined, yet had real potential. I watched as day after day "Mad Dog" pushed these two guys beyond their limits. Drill after drill, lap after lap. He was trying to get them in shape to make the team.

I will never forget the afternoon when these two guys rounded the far corner of the football field on lap five, and suddenly stopped in their tracks. Hands on their hips, heads hanging down, chests heaving for air—they gathered themselves for that long, lonely walk across the field to the coach.

What about you? Are you going to quit in the final lap because the going is too hard? Are you going to walk off the field and let your dream fade away? Or, are you going to hang tough and go the distance?

"You guys calling it quits?" the coach asked. "Yeah, coach," they answered, "it's harder than we thought it would be." "Alright, then," coach responded, "you guys get in shape and come back next season and try again."

With that the two walked off the field to the locker room. What happened next is why I remember this scene so vividly all these years later. The strength and conditioning coach, a hard-nosed disciplinarian dedicated to excellence, watched those two guys walk away—and his eyes filled with tears. "Damn," he quietly whispered, "those guys could've been champions. All they had to do was finish that last lap and they were on the team."

I was astounded to see how much he truly loved these guys, and how close they came to reaching their dreams—only to walk away. This was driven home with force a few months later when the University of Colorado football team played Notre Dame in the Orange Bowl and won a share of the 1990 National Championship.

Those two guys watched the game on TV—when they could have been playing on the field.

What about you? Are you going to quit in the final lap because the going is too hard? Are you going to walk off the field and let your dream fade away? Or, are you going to hang tough and go the distance?

The Bible says, "'Now the just shall live by faith; but if anyone draws back, My soul has no pleasure in him.' But we are not of those who draw back to perdition, but of those who believe to the saving of the soul" (Hebrews 10:38-39).

Guys, let me encourage you to renew your commitment even now to go the distance. By this point in your journey the glow of the recent Promise Keepers conference has faded, the routine of daily life has crowded the edges of your devotions, and maybe one or two guys have already missed a couple of your weekly meetings. It would be so easy right now to let it all slip away.

Unless we make a determined choice to pursue God's will on a daily basis, the relentless drift of life's circumstances will make our choices for us—and those choices will always be away from that which is the highest and best. No man ever drifts *to* God, but *away* from Him. Therefore, stir your hearts and provoke one another to go the distance!

You will recall how we discussed a few weeks ago that every man needs acceptance, affirmation, and accountability. He needs someone to look him right in the eye and say, "I love you; I believe in you; and, I'm committed to you being everything God has created you to be!" In fact, maybe now would be a good time for you to say this to one another in your small group.

Now, let's take a look at the man who called it quits.

A Sobering Situation

If a man is left without acceptance, affirmation, or accountability it will destroy him, or he will destroy himself. Such is the case of the worthless servant in our story today.

RISK

Luke 19:20-26, NKJV

"Then another came, saying, 'Master, here is your mina, which I have kept put away in a handkerchief. For I feared you, because you are an austere man. You collect what you did not deposit, and reap what you did not sow.' And he said to him, 'Out of your own mouth I will judge you, *you* wicked servant. You knew that I was an austere man, collecting what I did not deposit and reaping what I did not sow. Why then did you not put my money in the bank, that at my coming I might have collected it with interest?' And he said to those who stood by, 'Take the mina from him, and give *it* to him who has ten minas.' (But they said to him, 'Master, he has ten minas.') 'For I say to you, that to everyone who has will be given; and from him who does not have, even what he has will be taken away from him.'"

Five Facts about this Wicked Man

• He Believed a Lie

He offers his fear of the Lord as an excuse for his unfaithfulness. "I was afraid of you," he said, "because you are a hard man. You take out what you did not put in and reap what you did not sow." It is clear that this man did not know his Master, for his description could not be further from the truth.

How did he come to think such things? Quite obviously he listened to the lies that were being spread about the Nobleman; the very lies that caused the citizens earlier in the story to reject His Lordship.

> There are those in the Church who feel the need of religious affiliation to pacify their disturbed consciences, yet have no real motivation for actually serving Christ with their lives.

There is an enemy of Truth who goes about continually slandering Christ. He is antichrist in every sense of the word. His name is Satan. This man believed those lies, and in so doing sided with the devil and greatly dishonored his Lord. This pitiful man believed a lie, and he became a liar!

Are you believing any lies about Jesus?

• He Buried his Talent

The first words out of his mouth reek with hypocrisy—"Master," he said, "here is your mina, which I have kept put away in a handkerchief." This man did not truly regard Christ as his Master, or else he would have laid himself out to honor the Lord with his gifts. He was a phony. "Why call Me Lord, Lord," Jesus said on another occasion, "but do not do the things that I say?" Phonies talk a good game, but never deliver the goods.

There are those in the Church who feel the need for religious affiliation to pacify their disturbed consciences, yet have no real motivation for actually serving Christ with their lives. They content themselves to talk the language, but not actually live the life. Such men are false in their faith, and shallow in their affections; they profess to know Christ but deny Him by how they live.

The Bible speaks frankly about this kind of so-called Christian. Paul wrote, "They profess to know God, but in works they deny Him, being abominable, disobedient, and disqualified for every good work" (Titus 1:16). Jesus said, "Not everyone who says to Me, 'Lord, Lord,' shall enter the kingdom of heaven, but he who does the will of My Father in heaven" (Matthew 7:21). He then added these astounding words:

"Many will say to Me in that day, 'Lord, Lord, have we not prophesied in Your name, cast out demons in Your name, and done many wonders in Your name?' And then I will declare to them, 'I never knew you; depart from Me, you who practice lawlessness!'" (Matthew 7:22-23).

The Lord gave this man every opportunity, but he chose to bury the talent. Are you doing the same with your life? Are you letting your opportunities slip by unheeded? Are you neglecting the gifts that God has entrusted to you?

• He Blamed the Lord

"You are a hard man," he said to the Lord. In other words, this guy was saying, "I could have done something meaningful with my life, but you are so hard to deal with—so short-tempered and unfair—that I realized the best thing to do was to keep the talent you gave me safely hidden away so that you could have it back just like it was."

It started all the way back in the garden. Adam blamed God; and men have been blaming Him ever since. "The woman You gave me," Adam said. In other words, if the Lord had not given the woman to Adam—none of this would have ever happened. So, it's not Adam's fault, it's not even the woman's fault—it's God's!

Are you blaming God for something in your life?

• He Blew His Opportunity

The Lord ignored the man's insults and turned the argument back upon him. "Out of your own mouth I will judge you, you wicked servant. You knew that I was an austere man, collecting what I did not deposit and reaping what I did not sow. Why then did you not put my money in the bank, that at my coming I might have collected it with interest?"

The issue here is what did you do with what you were given? Your life matters to God. He did not haphazardly create you, nor randomly drop you into the gene pool of life. He created you with a purpose, and He has good reason to expect good returns on His investment in you.

This man blew his chance. Don't make the same mistake! His sobering failure stares each one of us squarely in the face, serving as a warning lest we let our own opportunities slip by unappreciated and unused.

• He Betrayed his Soul

This man had professed to be a servant of the Lord, but now his true colors were shown. Though he painted his face with the veneer of piety, his behavior betrayed the true condition of his soul. "You wicked servant," Jesus said to him. These are strong words, leaving no doubt about what the Lord thought. *Wicked* means "evil in thought and purpose." It is the fruit of following the devil.

Satan has but one agenda; to destroy everything that brings honor to Jesus Christ. He used this wicked man to do just that. Men, we must make sure that he does not do the same with us.

> **V**ision produces passion, and then, in turn, vision and passion produce discipline. Then, when these three are set in place, a man can (and will) take the greatest risks with his life to bring the highest honor to Christ.

As for the wicked servant, Jesus said, "Take from him and give it to another." Here we have the final, sobering summary of one man's desperate failure. He was disqualified, dishonored, and eternally damned. "Cast the unprofitable servant into the outer darkness," Jesus said. "There will be weeping and gnashing of teeth" (Matthew 25:30).

He no doubt thought he was doing the safe thing by burying his talent, keeping it from risk and loss; ready to give back to his Lord without incident. He clearly could not have been more mistaken! By taking no risk at all—he took the greatest risk of all, and in the end betrayed his own soul!

Conclusion

We have followed a basic theme throughout this 12-week adventure, summed up in four words—vision, passion, discipline, and risk. By now these words should be woven into your thoughts, and expressed more and more in your character. This is the life of the Noble Man.

We have demonstrated how vision produces passion, and then, in turn, vision and passion produce discipline. Then, when these three are set in place, a man can (and will) take the greatest risks with his life to bring the highest honor to Christ.

The wicked servant in our story failed at each of these crucial points. He had no compelling vision for his life, and he lived without any sense of passion. As a result he was undisciplined in every way, and unwilling to take any risk associated with serving Christ. He was the man who called it quits.

What about you?

Debriefing

1. How does this lesson impact your personal life?

2. Do you see in yourself any of the characteristics of the wicked servant?

3. Tell how others have positively shaped your life by acceptance, affirmation, and accountability.

4. What are some of the most common excuses men make for not being more spiritually active in today's world?

5. How can the other guys pray for you right now?

VISION

Wanted: Hazardous Men

Before We Get Started...

He was a Saint

There were two notorious and wicked brothers who terrorized a small town in the Midwest. When one of the brothers died it became the other's responsibility to make funeral arrangements. However, he could find no pastor in the county who would agree to officiate at the funeral.

It wasn't because they lacked compassion; it was because of the unusual request made by the surviving brother. He wanted the pastor to say of the deceased, "He was a saint." Of course, no pastor would agree to do such a dishonest thing.

In desperation, the brother offered $1,000 to any pastor who would say the words during the funeral, and one pastor agreed to do so. He was a prominent pastor of a prestigious church, and the entire community was shocked when they heard of his decision.

They all came to the funeral, not because they cared for the dead guy, but they wanted to see if the pastor would really compromise himself for a mere thousand dollars.

When the moment arrived and the pastor delivered the epithet without a stutter, "We all know that Charlie here was a wicked man. He was twisted, foul, perverse, and full of the devil. But compared to his brother...he was a saint!"

Wait...there's more!

A man cheated a church by watering down the paint for an exterior coat. As soon as he finished the job, a huge rain cloud appeared and poured down upon the paint, which washed off immediately. Then a voice spoke from the cloud, *"Repaint, and thin no more!"*

OK, Now Let's Get Serious...

Wanted: Hazardous Men

"Men who have hazarded their lives
for the name of the Lord Jesus."

Acts 15:26

Perhaps one of the greatest compliments ever paid one Christian by another occurred almost 2,000 years ago during a strategic meeting of the first disciples. The spread of Christianity had been explosive, with new churches springing up all throughout the Roman Empire. The challenge of balancing dynamic growth with uncompromised quality was very real—and continues to be so today. As the leaders in Jerusalem pondered how best to address this challenge, they chose two men to go forth with their blessings to represent Christ and His Gospel in the best possible way.

They chose Barnabas and Paul, men who, as the record shows, "hazarded their lives for the name of our Lord Jesus Christ" (Acts 15:26). O to God that such a thing could be said of us today!

They "hazarded their lives." The Greek meaning is "to surrender, to yield up, entrust, cast, commit, deliver up, give over." Inherent to the word is the idea of risk, especially in the face of danger. It means that another is now in control; another is now calling all the shots.

When was the last time you took a risk for Christ? Can others tell by how you live that your life has been "handed over" to Jesus?

May I ask when was the last time you took a risk for Christ? Can others tell by how you live that your life has been "handed over" to Jesus? As Christian men we are expected, dare I say *commanded*, to hand our lives over to Jesus Christ; to surrender our lives to Him, and His cause in this earth.

Contrary to what one may think this does not mean to be reckless or irresponsible. While there is unquestionable risk involved in "handing over your life to Christ," it is in fact the ultimate act of personal responsibility. Biblical endorsement comes from Jesus Himself. "Whoever loses his life for My sake will save it, but whoever insists on keeping his life will lose it" (Luke 9:24, Living Bible). C'mon guys; hand it over!

The Apostle Paul invites us to follow his example:

"I beseech you therefore, brethren, by the mercies of God, that ye present your bodies a living sacrifice, holy, acceptable unto God, which is your reasonable service. And be not conformed to this world: but be ye transformed by the renewing of

your mind, that ye may prove what is that good, and acceptable, and perfect, will of God." (Romans 12:1-2)

The noble spirit of true disciples does not seek the pampered, risk-free environment of a lifeless faith. No! It begs for challenge, and cries out for significance! You and I were created by God with an inner passion to live a life that makes a difference. But this will not happen until we "hand our lives over to Christ."

Only in His hands will we find the eternal security that emboldens us in this world to dare to think the unthinkable, to dream the unimaginable, and to do the impossible. Like the songwriter said, we are those who "dream the impossible dream, fight the unbeatable foe, bear with unbearable sorrow, and run where the brave dare not go."

We are those who will always seek "to right the unrightable wrong, and to fight for the right without question or pause; to be willing to pass into hell for a heavenly cause! And the world will be better for this, that one man scorned and covered in scars, still strove with his last ounce of courage to reach the unreachable star—and to dream the impossible dream!" (from the Broadway musical, *Man of La Mancha*, lyrics by Joe Darion).

Whether it be the fictional Don Quixote, or actual people that we ourselves know—we are faced daily with the stories of those who strive with all their hearts to achieve the spectacular in life, or in sports, or in business, or in education, or in exploration. These individuals have hazarded their lives for the sake of career, wealth, fame, fashion, or glory. Isn't it time that we hazarded our lives for the name of our Lord Jesus Christ?

Lord of the Rings

I have a championship ring. Actually, I have two. One is the Big Eight Conference Championship ring, the other is the 1990 National Championship ring. In the collegiate world of football it's a pretty big deal to win both. So you can imagine the excitement we all felt at Colorado when it happened. And though I was the chaplain, I was included when the rings were handed out. It's even got my name on it. Wow.

But there's just one problem. It doesn't fit. And I don't understand why. I was measured before the rings were made, and was eager to put them on when they arrived. But, no, it was too small. Both of them!

I stood there in my room trying to figure out a way to make them fit me, but nothing I did would work. I put spit on my finger and was able to force the ring over my knuckle, but then my finger swelled up like a hot dog. I was barely able to get the ring off before it was too late.

Do you know what a drag it is to have two championship rings that you can't wear? I remember muttering under my breath a half-hearted complaint to the Lord about this. "It's too small," I said. And then one of those moments that you never forget happened—the Lord spoke to my heart and said, "That's right. It *is* too small. I have called you to something bigger than football games and championship rings."

As a chaplain I watched a football team devote themselves with Spartan-like dedication to a cause that ultimately, on the grand stage of life, is short-lived and soon forgotten by all but those who paid the price to win it. My question is this: if these guys would pay so dearly for that which means so little, what in the world is holding us back from giving it all for Christ! In the words of Paul, "They do it to obtain a corruptible crown, but we an incorruptible" (1 Corinthians 9:25). Shouldn't our dedication exceed theirs to the same degree that our prize excels theirs? Indeed, it should!

> If these guys would pay so dearly for that which means so little, what in the world is holding us back from giving it all for Christ!

Take A Minute...

Read the following Scriptures and write the one word that comes to mind from each verse:

- 1 Corinthians 9:24-27 _____

- Philippians 3:14 _____

- 1 Timothy 4:8 _____

- 1 Timothy 6:12 _____

- 2 Timothy 2:5 _____

- 2 Timothy 4:7-8 _____

- Hebrews 12:1-4 _____

The words that I thought of are: Discipline, Intensity, Godliness, Commitment, Integrity, Faithfulness, and Vision. Yours may be similar to mine, or totally different. One thing is sure—the Lord has called each one of us to hazard our lives for the honor of His name. And it will require an undeniable display of vision, passion, discipline, and risk to obey Him fully.

PROMISE KEEPERS®
MEN OF INTEGRITY

Once to Every Man and Nation

Years ago I came across an old hymn by an unknown songwriter. We don't sing it any more, and that's too bad. Some of those old songs have a message that is desperately needed in our day. In fact, guys, let me encourage you to do something you'll never regret. Pick up an old hymnal (the older, the better), and at least once a week just read the words to the songs. You'll find treasures like this:

Once to every man and nation
comes the moment to decide
In the strife of truth with falsehood
for the good or evil side.
Some great cause some great decision
offering each the bloom or blight
And that choice goes by forever
between that darkness and that light.
Then to side with truth is noble
when we share her wretched crust;
Ere her cause bring fame and fortune,
and 'tis prosperous to be just.
Then it is the brave man chooses
while the cowards stand aside
Until a multitude make virtue
of a Faith they had denied.

OK! Sign Me Up!

"Alright, preacher," I hear you say, "you got me! I'm ready to hand it over to Jesus and storm Hell with a water pistol! What do I do now?" That's a good question, and I can only tell you this as an answer. In the words of the prophet Micah, "He has shown you, O man, what is good; and what does the LORD require of you, but to do justly, and to love mercy, and to walk humbly with your God?" (Micah 6:8, NKJV). This verse sums up the essence of a godly man's life; a man whose life is handed over to Jesus; a Hazardous Man! It tells us three things:

We are to be men of Justice. Micah was a peasant prophet speaking up to the civil powers that ruled in Jerusalem. It is worthy to note that the justice issue is always raised from below, not from above. In other words, those in power never see a need to change anything—they like it the way it is.

Think about it guys. Have you ever been in a situation that was unfair, where you were being taken advantage of by another who had all the power? Have you ever been cheated out of what was rightfully yours by clever, legal maneuvers made by those who know how to bend the rules for their own selfish purposes? Have you ever been betrayed by someone you trusted, and now—because the pain is so deep—find it almost impossible to trust them again?

Now let me be very direct. Men of color can answer these questions with many, many examples from their personal lives—some very painful; while most of us who are Caucasian have to search our memories for a time when anything like this ever happened to us.

We are the ones in power, and the system works fine for us. But it does not work for our brothers! This is a gross inequity; and to know it, and then permit it to continue, is a diabolic injustice.

The Lord has called us to Himself, and commanded us to love one another. Oswald Chambers wrote, "Love is not an attribute of God, it is God; whatever God is, love is. If your concept of love does not agree with justice, judgment, purity, and holiness, then your idea of love is wrong."

The Bible says, "The LORD does what is right and fair for all who are oppressed" (Psalm 103:6). As men of God, we will do the same. We are to follow that which is altogether just—defending the poor and fatherless, doing justice for the afflicted and needy. Indeed, "pure religion and undefiled before God and the Father is this, to visit the fatherless and widows in their affliction, and to keep himself unspotted from the world" (James 1:27). This will require vision, passion, discipline, and risk.

> We are to follow that which is altogether just—defending the poor and fatherless, doing justice for the afflicted and needy.

> If you will agree with God and submit to His will for your life, He will make you a man of justice and mercy; clothed with humility!

We are to be men of Mercy. Solomon wrote, "Let not mercy and truth forsake thee" (Proverbs 3:3), assuring us that they would bring us favor and good understanding in the sight of God and man. Truth without mercy is harsh; mercy without truth is irresponsible. Together they form the essence of godliness. "God works powerfully," wrote John Newton, "but for the most part gently and gradually."

Justice calls for action against that which is wrong; mercy requires patience in dealing with those who have been wronged. Together they accomplish God's will in our sphere of influence. Guys, you and I can't change the world, but we can do something about what goes on where we live. The light that shines the farthest, shines brightest at home.

Let me ask you a question. When you see a report on the news about some problem in a neighborhood across town—a drug problem, a crime problem, an economic problem—do you intuitively think, "That's *their* problem" or "That's *my* problem"? What if the tables were turned? Would you want others to see your struggles as though they were their own—especially if they had the power to do something about it?

The Bible says, "Do not withhold good from those to whom it is due, when it is in the power of your hand to do so" (Proverbs 3:27, NKJV), and, "to him that knows to do good, and does it not, to him it is sin" (James 4:17). Christ Himself summed up the entire Law and Prophets in one word: *Love* (Mark 12:29-31).

Paul wrote it this way, "Owe no one anything except to love one another, for he who loves another has fulfilled the law. For the commandments, 'You shall not commit adultery,' 'You shall not murder,' 'You shall not steal,' 'You shall not bear false witness,' 'You shall not covet,' and if there is any other commandment, are all summed up in this saying, namely, 'You shall love your neighbor as yourself.' Love does no harm to a neighbor; therefore love is the fulfillment of the law" (Romans 13:8-10, NKJV).

As men we are to act justly, and love tenderly. This will require vision, passion, discipline, and risk.

We are to be men of Humility. Pride has no place in the presence of the Lord, nor in the service we render unto His name. Pride will never do justice, for it only seeks its own. Pride will never show mercy, because it delights in the power of death. Pride will never walk with God, for it sees itself to be equal to the Most High. Thus, God resists the proud, but gives grace to the humble.

Humility is the God-given self assurance that eliminates the need to prove to others the worth of who you are, and the rightness of what you do. It is the freedom to be yourself before God, and before others. Humility is the result of being in total agreement with the Lord. "Can two walk together except they be agreed?" (Amos 3:3).

DISCIPLINE

PROMISE
KEEPERS®
MEN OF INTEGRITY

If you will agree with God and submit to His will for your life, He will make you a man of justice and mercy; clothed with humility! And He will anoint you with His grace. His power and ability will use your limited resources in His unlimited ways. Even if all you have is two fish and five loaves of bread—there is going to a banquet in your sphere of influence!

Men, as we walk humbly with our God, He works powerfully through our obedience. And the work He does not only brings fame to Christ — but "good tidings of great joy to all people!" (Luke 2:10).

O, Lord, let it be so even today.

Debriefing

1. Tell of a time when you took a risk for Jesus.

2. What is your impossible dream?

3. In what ways have you settled for something too small instead of going after what God has called you to do?

4. What part of this lesson disturbs you the most, and why?

5. What is one thing you will do this week that enacts justice, exalts mercy, and demonstrates humility? Write it down, and ask your friends to hold you to it:

   _____

   _____

   _____

   _____

   _____

6. How can the other guys pray for you right now?

WEEK ELEVEN

What a Day it Will Be!

Before We Get Started...

A sailor was atop the mast in the crow's nest looking for land when a big gust of wind blew him from his perch. He fell with such force that he crashed through the deck and landed in the Captain's quarters. Realizing he was in the presence of his Captain, the sailor jumped to attention and snapped a salute. The Captain stared in disbelief. "Are you alright, sailor?" He asked. "Aye, sir," the sailor replied, "I've been through hardships before!"

Well, since you liked that one so much...

There was a man who loved to make up puns. One day a local magazine sponsored a pun-contest. The man entered the contest ten different times in the hope that at least one of his puns would win. Unfortunately, no pun in ten did.

Wait...there's more!

A preacher and a bus driver both died on the same day and arrived within seconds of one another at the Pearly Gates. Saint Peter met them there and took them both in at the same time. Since the bus driver arrived before the preacher, Peter took him to his heavenly mansion first. It was glorious—and just two doors down from Jesus!

"Oh glory to God!" the preacher thought within himself. "If the bus driver gets this place, I'm sure the house right next to Jesus is for me." But Peter turned the other direction and led the preacher all the way to the other end of the street where there stood a quaint cottage with a few flowers in the front yard. "What's this?" the preacher exclaimed. "I preached the Gospel for forty years and get a bungalow, and a bus driver gets a mansion?"

"Well," Peter calmly replied, "what you don't realize is that when you preached—people fell to sleep. But, when that guy drove his bus—they prayed!"

OK, Now Let's Get Serious...

What A Day it Will Be!

"Well done, good and faithful servant; you have been
faithful over a few things, I will make you ruler over many things.
Enter into the joy of your Lord."

Matthew 25:23

And now we speak of things so sublime that they are far beyond the scope of man's imagination. Indeed, we could never even conceive of such things as we are about to discuss. As it is written, "Eye hath not seen, nor ear heard, neither have entered into the heart of man, the things which God hath prepared for them that love him" (1 Corinthians 2:9).

Dream of heaven, O dreamer of dreams, and your dreams at best are altogether vanity—for God is able to do exceeding abundantly above all that we could ever even think or imagine.

How then do we know of these glorious things, seeing they are beyond our ability to know them? "God has revealed them to us by his Spirit," the Bible says, "for the Spirit searches all things, yes, the deep things of God" (1 Corinthians 2:10, NKJV). The verse goes on to say that we have been given the Spirit of God "that we might know the things that are freely given to us by God" (vs.12).

> By living each day now with *that* Day fully in mind—our choices, our conduct, and our conversations will become much more intentional.

Why is it important that we speak now of things that are yet so far away? Jesus regarded our future in heaven an important motivation for faithful service during this time of waiting for His return. That's why He included it in the Parable of the Talents. And that's why we ought to familiarize ourselves with what the Bible says on this subject.

We will discover that by living each day now with *that* Day fully in mind—our choices, our conduct, and our conversations will become much more intentional as it pertains to bringing honor to Jesus by faithfully obeying His word and doing His will.

In *Knowing God* J.I. Packer wrote, "Living becomes an awesome business when you realize that you spend every moment of your life in the sight and company of an omniscient, omnipresent Creator."

He sees us; and one day, we will see Him.

What a day it will be when we see Jesus! One of my favorite Bible verses comes from the Wuest New Testament. It sums up how we will feel when we stand before the Lord and see all He has done in His love for us:

"And they were completely flabbergasted, and that in a super abundant degree, which itself was augmented by the addition of yet more astonishment, saying, 'He has done all things well!'" (Mark 7:37).

And on *that* Day when we shall look upon Him, men, wouldn't it be wonderful to hear the Lord say to each of us in return, "You, too, have done all things well! Now, enter into the joy of your Lord!"

It can happen; and for some of us—it will!

Praise, As We Have Never Heard Before

Everybody knows that the choir in Heaven is solid gold, and we know that the worship there is endless. But what most of us don't realize is that our first days in glory are going to be filled with praise—praise, as we have never heard before. It will not be the sound of our voices praising God. No. Rather, it will be the astounding sound of God—are you ready for this?—praising us!

You don't believe me? Listen to what the Bible says:

"Therefore judge nothing before the time, until the Lord comes, who will both bring to light the hidden things of darkness and reveal the counsels of the hearts. Then each one's praise will come from God" (1 Corinthians 4:5, NKJV).

Only God knows what is in a man's heart; He alone sees and understands the deepest secrets, the fondest hopes, the truest motives—even when these are somewhat soiled by our own carnality. This is why we are expressly told to not judge one another. The truth is we do not know what is in another man's heart; we only know what is in our own. Our judgment of another, then, is the trumpeting aloud of our own hidden faults.

The best policy is always to obey God's Word. It says, "Judge nothing before the time." What time is that? It is the time when the Lord comes back. "He will bring to light the hidden things of darkness and reveal the counsels of the hearts." Oh, this could be bad.

I remember as a kid dreading the thought of the Day of Judgment. Somehow I got it in my head that on *that* Day God was going to stand me naked in the middle of a huge arena and bring all my sins out into the open for everybody to see. The vast crowd was going to moan and wince with each pitiful display of my disobedience. And then the Lord was going to really let me have it. To be honest, I wasn't looking forward to going to heaven.

RISK

But this idea of mine never made sense with the other parts of Scripture that talk about how my sins have been forgiven—and forgotten. Somehow I failed to make a distinction between God's judgment of my sin, which happened on the cross when Jesus paid it all; and, God's judgment of my works that would happen before the Judgment Seat of Christ on *that* Day. This speaks of two different kinds of judgment.

I was truly stumped about this until a phrase of Scripture caught my eye. Did you catch it earlier when we first read the verse? It plainly says, "Then each one's praise will come from God." What's this? God is going to *praise* us? Each one of us? This changes everything!

> When you and I stand before the Lord He is going to bring out into the open all the undeveloped gifts, abilities, treasures, dreams, and possibilities, and show what He had in mind all along.

This means that the hidden things of darkness and the counsels of the hearts are *good* things—praiseworthy things. In other words, when you and I stand before the Lord He is going to bring out into the open all the undeveloped gifts, abilities, treasures, dreams, and possibilities, and show what He had in mind all along when He created us. He is going to show how these things stirred our deepest imaginations and filled us with holy desire to live for Him—even if we did not fully realize it all. And then He is going to publicly render His opinion, His judgment, about these things and then—here it comes—give us praise!

Imagine it; the Lord Himself praising you for the way you lived your life in honor of His name! What a day that will be!

The Lord knows what's in your heart, and He sees each deed done for His glory—great or small. And on that glorious day when we stand before Him in the assembly of the ages, we will hear Him openly declare for all to hear the depth of His admiration for even the simplest moments of our faithful service!

But There is More

Not only will the Lord render to every man the praise his life is due, but—oh, I can hardly write the words, for they are so foreign to our thoughts; and I can only write them because Jesus Himself said that it would be so—Christ will then "gird Himself, have them sit down to eat, and will come and serve them" (Luke 12:37)! Now you know how Peter felt when Jesus stooped to wash his feet; or, how John felt when Jesus bowed before him to be baptized. But there's more!

God will reward each one with an eternal weight of glory. As joint-heirs with Christ, we will be made to shine as the sun in the kingdom of our Father (Romans 8:17, Matthew 13:43). And we will reign with Him forever (Revelation 20:4). But there's still more! We will be given crowns that are incorruptible:

- The Crown of Life—James 1:12
- The Crown of Righteousness—2 Timothy 4:8
- The Crown of Glory—1 Peter 5:4
- The Crown of Rejoicing—1 Thessalonians 2:19

And, of course you know what we will do with those crowns? We will fall down in worship before Him who sits on the throne, and cast our crowns before His feet, saying: "You are worthy, O Lord, to receive glory and honor and power!" (Revelation 4:10). Oh, what a day that will be!

Heaven; don't miss it for the world!

Meanwhile Back at the Ranch

Remember, when we started this journey several weeks back we took the Parable of the Talents as our primary biblical point of reference. The Bible not only tells us the story, but also lets us know *why* Jesus told it. "He told a story to correct the impression that the kingdom of God would begin right away" (Luke 19:11, New Living Translation).

Jesus wanted the people to know then—and us to know now—that the time between His first and second coming would be longer than anybody expected. He also wanted us to know what He expected of us during this time of waiting for the Lord's return—faithfulness in our stewardship of the talents, gifts, opportunities, and responsibilities granted to us during the course of our lives. And, finally, He wanted to motivate us with the idea of eternal rewards so that we would each give our highest and best for His Name's sake while we live on this earth.

Take a Minute….

As a group take the next few minutes and discuss your thoughts about the following Scriptures:

- Matthew 5:12
- Matthew 10:41-42
- Matthew 16:27
- Luke 6:35
- 1 Corinthians 3:8
- 1 Corinthians 3:14
- Colossians 3:24
- Hebrews 10:35
- 2 John 1:8
- Revelation 22:12

Robert Louis wrote, "A godly man accepts responsibility, rejects passivity, leads courageously, and expects the greater reward." Men, Jesus expects us to expect great rewards in heaven. And for those who say, "Oh, I'm not interested in rewards; I'll be happy just to be in heaven with Jesus." Well, with a pitiful attitude like that, what makes you so sure that He will want you there! I'm sure the guy who buried his talents was thinking the same thing—and look what happened to him!

Hey, if eternal rewards are important enough for Jesus to tell us about them, then they are important enough to stir our hearts with vision, passion, discipline, and risk to go all out to win them—for the honor of Christ's name alone!

The Apostle Paul, following Christ's example, also uses the idea of eternal rewards as motivation. "If any man builds on this foundation using gold, silver, costly stones, wood, hay or straw, his work will be shown for what it is, because the Day will bring it to light. It will be revealed with fire, and the fire will test the quality of each man's work. If what he has built survives, he will receive his reward. If it is burned up, he will suffer loss; he himself will be saved, but only as one escaping through the flames" (1 Corinthians 3:12-15, NIV).

> **I**f eternal rewards are important enough for Jesus to tell us about them, then they are important enough to stir our hearts with vision, passion, discipline, and risk to go all out to win them—for the honor of Christ's name alone!

Now, guys, let me ask you a simple and direct question. When the Lord tests the quality of your life's work for His name, which would you rather be? The guy whose work passed, because it was built with gold, silver, and precious stones—or, the guy whose work failed because it was built with wood, hay, and stubble? (I know it's a tough question, so I'll give you a few minutes to answer. You can even talk amongst yourselves to make sure you get the answer right.)

Of course we want to be the guy who passes the test. Duh. Paul wanted the same thing for himself. His vision, passion, discipline, and risk-taking stemmed from this one over-ruling goal. In his own words, "We make it our goal to please Him, whether we are at home in the body or away from it. For we must all appear before the judgment seat of Christ, that each one may receive what is due him for the things done while in the body, whether good or bad" (2 Corinthians 5:9-10, NIV).

John put it this way, "Beloved, now we are children of God; and it has not yet been revealed what we shall be, but we know that when He is revealed, we shall be like Him, for we shall see Him as He is. And everyone who has this hope in Him purifies himself, just as He is pure" (1 John 3:2-3, NKJV).

Men, the promise of Christ's return, and the hope of eternal rewards, have provided saints down through the ages the strongest motivation for service and the greatest comfort during hardships suffered for Christ's sake. It will be worth it all when we see Jesus.

He is coming back—sooner or later.

So Why the Long Delay?

Why has He waited so long? And how much longer will it be? Two thousand years and counting tends to make one think it isn't going to happen at all. So why the long delay? The Bible says, "A day or a thousand years from now is like tomorrow to the Lord. He isn't really being slow about His promised return, even though it sometimes seems that way. But He is waiting, for the good reason that He is not willing that any should perish, and He is giving more time for sinners to repent" (2 Peter 3:9, Living Bible).

If by some chance you happen to be reading this and you have not yet given your life to Jesus Christ—get a clue! You're the very one who is holding this whole thing up! He is waiting for *you*! And so is everybody else. Give your life to Jesus, and let's get out of here!

By the way, guys, how you doing with your list of five friends? Remember back when we started, I asked you to make of list of five friends who you wanted to see come to Christ? Well, what's happened? Have you seen any progress? Have you done anything to let them know you are praying for them? Have you shared your faith with them in any way?

Vision, passion, discipline, and risk. Get it?

Conclusion

"Then the King will say to those on his right, 'Come, you who are blessed by my Father; take your inheritance, the kingdom prepared for you since the creation of the world. For I was hungry and you gave me something to eat, I was thirsty and you gave me something to drink, I was a stranger and you invited me in, I needed clothes and you clothed me, I was sick and you looked after me, I was in prison and you came to visit me.'

"Then the righteous will answer him, 'Lord, when did we see you hungry and feed you, or thirsty and give you something to drink? When did we see you a stranger and invite you in, or needing clothes and clothe you? When did we see you sick or in prison and go to visit you?'

"The King will reply, 'I tell you the truth, whatever you did for one of the least of these brothers of mine, you did for me'" (Matthew 25:34-40, NIV).
Oh, what a day that will be!

Even so, come Lord Jesus

Debriefing

1. Does the thought of Christ's appearing fill you with joy, or fear?

2. What would you do differently if you could actually see the Lord standing beside you day by day?

3. What do you think about the idea of God praising you?

4. What praiseworthy things do you see in the other guys in your group?

5. How will the truths of this lesson affect the way you live?

6. How can the other guys pray for you right now?

WEEK TWELVE

How Then Shall We Live?

Before We Get Started...

Apastor realized there were no donations from the church's most successful businessman. So he called him to persuade him to contribute. "Our records show that out of a yearly income of at least $5,000,000, you have not given anything to the church. Wouldn't you like to give back to the Lord in some way?"

The man mulled this over for a moment and replied, "First, do your records also show that my mother is dying after a long illness, and has medical bills that are several times her annual income? Or that my brother, a disabled veteran, is blind and confined to a wheelchair? Or that my sister's husband died in a traffic accident leaving her penniless with three children?!"

Embarrassed, the pastor responded, "We had no idea you were going through such..." But, before he could finish, the man interrupted him, "So if I don't give any money to them, why should I give any to you?"

Wait...there's more!

A pastor was hiking when he came upon a shepherd tending a large flock. "If I can guess how many sheep you have," the pastor asked, "can I take my pick of the flock?" The shepherd thought it unlikely that this stranger could guess the exact number, so he agreed.

The pastor looked the sheep over for a minute and then said, "You have 437 sheep." The shepherd was dumbfounded. "That's exactly right! How could you ever have guessed that?" "Oh it's nothing really," the pastor answered, "I just have a knack for sizing up crowds." He then took his pick of the flock and draped it across his shoulder as he headed for home.

Seeing him walk away, the shepherd got an idea. "Say, mister; before you go—if I can guess your occupation, can I have my sheep back?" The pastor thought to himself, "There is no way he could ever guess what I do," and so he said, "Sure, give it a shot." The shepherd looked at him for a moment and said, "You are a pastor." The pastor's mouth dropped open. "That's amazing," he said. "How did you ever guess that?!" The shepherd replied, "If you'll put my dog down, I'll tell you."

OK, Now Let's Get Serious...

How Then Shall We Live?

Let your light so shine before men, that they may see your good works,
and glorify your Father which is in heaven.

Matthew 5:16

September 11, 2001, 8:46 a.m. in New York City—19 men, blinded by religious bigotry and enraged by a hatred of freedom, unleashed an act of unimaginable terror against unsuspecting men, women, and children. The world watched helplessly as thousands of our fellow citizens perished in the combined disasters of the World Trade Center, the Pentagon, and the crashed airliner in the ploughed fields of Pennsylvania.

President George W. Bush stood before Congress and delivered what has been touted as the single most compelling speech ever given by a U.S. President under any circumstances. In that speech he spoke of a long war.

A new day has dawned in our world. Business as usual is no longer possible. An enemy has emerged from the shadows and shown his complete disregard for life, liberty, truth, justice, freedom, and civility. Hardened to reason, cold-hearted toward love, and lost in the babble of incantations, this cowardly foe strikes out against all—the aged, the young, the defenseless, and the innocent. It matters not in the least to this adversary who may perish—including even themself.

> If ever the time was right and the opportunity great for men of God to champion truth in a time of error, to advance righteousness in a time of terror—it is now.

And so we are all on watch. None is afforded the luxury of distance from the front lines—for the front lines are now everywhere, as terror can strike anywhere...at any time.

If ever the time was right and the opportunity great for men of God to champion truth in a time of error, to advance righteousness in a time of terror—it is now. If ever there was a time to let our lights shine before men, it is now. And the times have fallen upon us to answer the call. Indeed we are those "upon whom the ends of the ages has come" (1 Corinthians 10:11).

How then shall we live?

We shall live as men of vision, passion, discipline, and risk.

Vision—the ability to see beyond your limitations

Helen Keller was once asked, "Is there anything worse than being blind?" "Yes," she replied without hesitation, "having eyesight, but no vision." Pity the man, and the nation, that has no vision. Solomon said, "Where there is no vision, the people perish" (Proverbs 29:18). The word "perish" means to cast off restraints, to live without boundaries.

Take vision away from a man, and he will cast himself to the wind—doing whatever he feels like doing, whenever he feels like doing it, with little regard to what it will cost him, or to how it affects others. The consequence of such behavior is destruction and ruin. Indeed, much of the trouble in today's world can be traced to the lack of vision in the hearts of men.

Vision empowers us to deny the lure of lesser things and scale the summit of that which is sublime. Nehemiah gave a stirring example of this in his answer to those who tried to get him to stop the work of the Lord: "I am carrying on a great work and cannot go down. Why should the work stop while I leave it and go down to you?" (Nehemiah 6:3).

Are you like Nehemiah? Are you carrying on a great work for the Lord in your personal life, in your home, at your job or in your classroom, and in your community? Do you, like Nehemiah, have the inner strength to withstand the temptation to compromise and surrender? In other words, do you have a vision?

A.W. Tozer wrote, "God is looking for those through who He can do the impossible. What a pity that we settle for only those things we can do ourselves." Godly vision creates enthusiasm, defines boundaries, generates activity, unites effort, rallies us to a noble purpose, and supplies us with all the necessary elements for fully doing the will of God.

How then shall we live? We shall live as men of vision—vision that produces passion.

Passion—being empowered by a noble dream

Vision produces passion as surely as a spark ignites a fire. A man will never be moved to the highest level of obedience and effectiveness apart from a deep inner passion that is born of a noble vision. Remember, big dreams create the magic that stirs men's souls to greatness. Nothing significant was ever achieved without passion.

Yet much of what occurs in many of today's churches is all but void of godly passion. A critic once said to an audience of professing Christians, "If one tenth of what you believe is true, you should be ten times as excited as you are!" Indeed.

PASSION

Webster's defines passion as "an intense, compelling emotion, evidenced in decisive and courageous action." The greatest achievements in life are usually accomplished by people who have a singular desire that becomes the ruling passion of all they do.

What noble vision rises on the horizon of your future with such radiance that the shadows of insignificant living fade quickly into the past? What grand thing makes your heart beat faster, your pace quicken with zeal, and your thoughts race with endless possibilities of a life well spent?

"The future," wrote Thomas Cahill, "may be germinating today in some unheralded corner where a great-hearted human being is committed to loving outcasts in an extraordinary way." What's happening in your unheralded corner of the world?

> **What grand thing makes your heart beat faster, your pace quicken with zeal, and your thoughts race with endless possibilities of a life well spent?**

The Lord commended Phinehas, Aaron's grandson, for displaying a passionate zeal among the people on the Lord's behalf. "He was zealous for the honor of his God," the Lord said (Numbers 25:13, NIV). Could the same be said of you and me?

How then shall we live? We shall live as men of vision and passion; knowing that vision and passion produce discipline.

Discipline—embracing the restraints of a godly aspiration

Isaiah the prophet wrote, "The noble man makes noble plans, and by noble deeds he stands" (Isaiah 32:8, NIV). Discipline is what separates dreamers from achievers. Coach Bill McCartney told his team, "Greatness comes through the discipline of attending to the details." Champions do not simply will themselves into victory; they also work very hard, many times going over the same thing again and again—until they get it right.

"Successful people have the habit of doing the things that failures do not like to do;" wrote Albert Gray, "they don't like doing them either, necessarily, but their dislike is subordinated to the strength of their purpose." Discipline is the difference between winners and losers.

The one reoccurring entry in the diary of Christopher Columbus speaks volumes, and navigates the right course for us: "This day we sailed on." Some days, that's enough. Ours is a long obedience in the same direction. Andrew Murray wrote, "There can be no guidance that is not perpetual." In other words, we don't pick and choose when we will obey. Jesus asked, "Why do you keep on saying that I am your Lord, when you refuse to do what I say?" (Luke 6:46, Century English Version).

Hearing the voice of the Lord, knowing His will, and doing what pleases Him—all stem from being disciplined by His Spirit. "Blessed is the man You discipline, O LORD, the man You teach from Your law" (Psalm 94:12, NIV).

The writer of Hebrews said, "No discipline seems pleasant at the time, but painful. Later on, however, it produces a harvest of righteousness and peace for those who have been trained by it" (12:11, NIV). Discipline is not always pleasant; but the payoff is extraordinary! Tom Landry said, "A coach is a man who makes men do what they don't want to do, so that they can become what they've always wanted to be." Should the Lord do any less?

How then shall we live? We shall live as men of vision, of passion, and of discipline—knowing that God has called us to risk everything for the honor of His name.

Risk—spending your life to make a difference

The interesting thing about fear and faith is that, in one sense, they are both the same—both believe that what you can't see will happen. But fear renders a man powerless; unable to decide intelligently, or act decisively. Faith, on the other hand, empowers a man to see the invisible, and do the impossible. And both—fear and faith alike—involve great risk.

In the parable of the talents Jesus baffled the disciples when He commanded that the one talent be taken from the unfaithful servant and given to the one who had ten. "But, Lord," they said, "he already has ten." And Jesus replied, "Risk your life and get more than you ever dreamed of. Play it safe and end up holding the bag" (Luke 19:26, The Message).

Following the path of least resistance is what makes rivers crooked—men, too. Guys, surely you realize by now that there is no way to live a life fully devoted to Christ without taking some risk. The apostle Paul told young Timothy, "Anyone who wants to live all out for Christ is in for a lot of trouble; there's no getting around it" (2 Timothy 3:12, The Message). Guys, you and I are like teabags—not worth much until we are put in some hot water.

Isn't it time you lived all out for Christ? "What if I fail?" you may be wondering. Somebody once said, "I would rather fail while attempting something great for Christ, than to succeed at doing nothing at all." Ditto.

The Psalmists prayed, "I am always ready to risk my life; I have not forgotten your law" (Psalm 119:109, Good News Bible). The New Living Translation puts it this way. "My life constantly hangs in the balance, but I will not stop obeying your law."

Peter Drucker wrote, "There is nothing so useless as doing with great efficiency that which should not be done at all." That being true, then there is nothing more exhilarating than daring to do that which should be done—especially when no one else wants to do it!

"No living creature, except for a man, is able to take a risk for the sake of Truth—even the risk of death." These words were said by Russian Orthodox priest Aleksandr Menn shortly before he was executed for his faith in Christ. C'mon guys, what risk are you wiling to take for Truth?

J. B. Phillips said, "Anyone who opens his personality to the living Spirit takes a risk of being considerably shaken." I would add that anyone thus shaken by God will most likely shake up the world in which they live, move, and have their being.

How then shall we live? We shall live as men of vision, passion, discipline, and risk—for the honor of Christ, and the good of all those within the sphere of our influence.

A Word of Warning

> I would rather fail while attempting something great for Christ, than to succeed at doing nothing at all.

These four work together—vision, passion, discipline, and risk. Any one without the others is a sure setup for trouble. Let me explain.

Risk without discipline is recklessness. In the days of Moses several men lost their lives as they rushed ahead to possess the Promised Land without the Lord's presence. Moses said, "This will not succeed! Do not go up, because the LORD is not with you. You will be defeated by your enemies" (Numbers 14:41-42, NIV). The Bible says, "Nevertheless, in their presumption they went up" (vs.44). And they were defeated. They thought they were brave and decisive; instead, they were only reckless. And it cost them their very lives.

Discipline without passion is legalism. G. Campbell Morgan noted, "It is possible to be biblically correct, doctrinally pure, theologically sound, morally impeccable, and spiritually useless!" Legalism will do that to a guy. "The letter killeth, but the Spirit giveth life" (2 Corinthians 3:6). How pitiful the man that cannot discern between the two.

There is no heart so hard, no mind so darkened, and no hand so cruel as one that is ensnared in legalism. Charles Spurgeon, that Prince of Preachers, said, "Any virtue practiced to perfection can become a vice. Prudence can become negligence; honesty become cruelty; self-respect become vain glory; justice

become heartlessness; and chastity become barrenness." May God deliver us from self-serving, self-righteous know-it-alls who think everybody else but them is headed straight for hell.

Passion without vision is hype. Have you ever watched TV at 3 a.m.? There's not a lot on. You can catch reruns of WWF Championship matches, or Christian broadcasting. Those are your choices. And as you surf back and forth between these two, you end up asking the same question about both: *"Is this for real?"*

There is a lot of bravado in many pulpits across our world. Small men boasting great things to garner unto themselves the adoration that belongs to Jesus alone. I've been in some churches where I couldn't tell if the guy was trying to save my soul or sell me a used car. Both sounded like the best deal I'd ever come across! Yada. Yada. Yada.

Vision without Jesus is meaningless. As a young man I recall a preacher saying, "You've but one life, 'twill soon be past; only what's done for Christ will last." That has stayed with me all these years later.

Jesus will return one day, and when He does there are so many, many things that simply will not matter any more. Doesn't it just make sense, then, that the best of our talents, our abilities, our resources, our labors, and even our very lives be dedicated to the things that matter most to Him?

Debriefing

1. How has life been different for you since September 11, 2001?

2. Give an example of a time when you were able to resist temptation because of the vision God has given you for your life.

3. What would your friends say you are the most passionate about?

4. Tell of a time when the Lord disciplined you and, though it was unpleasant, it turned out for the best.

5. What would you say is one thing that keeps you from taking a risk for Christ?

6. How can the other guys pray for you right now?

Epilogue

"Launch out into the deep and
let down your nets for a catch."

Luke 5:4, NKJV

The deed is done. You now hold in your hands a workbook that has been worked, and, hopefully has worked on you. No doubt you're surprised by how quickly the 12 weeks have passed. Why, it seems like only the other day you guys started. Now what? Where do you go from here? What's the next step for you, O noble man?

May I make a suggestion? Why not take this workbook and do it again—with four or five other guys? Think about it. One of the surest ways to keep what you have received is to give it away to others! By passing it on, you actually strengthen its place in your own heart.

Paul told young Timothy the same thing I am suggesting to you. "The things that you have heard from me among many witnesses," he said, "commit these to faithful men who will be able to teach others also" (2 Timothy 2:2, NKJV).

We've taught you about vision, passion, discipline, and risk. Now it's time to see if the lesson took. It's time for you to "launch out into the deep and let down your nets for a catch." The Lord is in your boat—He won't let you sink!

And though it seems like a small thing you're being asked to do, consider the staggering possibilities of what could happen if you do it.

Let's say that over 200,000 men attended the Storm the Gates conference this year. (A likely figure based on early registration trends). And let's say that all of them decided to participate in a small group and work through this book for 12 weeks. Where does that put us right now? Two hundred thousand guys, including you, are ready to take the next step!

Let's say each one of them formed another group of five guys and took them through the book. In just 12 short weeks, together we will reach 1,000,000 men! Not bad. Now consider what would happen if each of those guys did the same thing again.

That's another 5,000,000 men—who, in turn do it again and reach another 25,000,000. And with just one more pass at it, together we can touch 125,000,000 men for the honor of Jesus Christ. That is virtually every man in America! All in one year.

Surely in light of so great an opportunity, you can do your part and just lead five other guys for the next 12 weeks. What d'ya say?

About the Author

James Ryle, author and speaker, has been involved in full time ministry since 1972, serving as pastor of two churches in Colorado. James also served as the chaplain for the University of Colorado football team from 1989 to 1998. He is the President of Truth*Works* Ministries, ministering as an evangelist and conference speaker throughout the US, Canada, and Europe. In addition, James is one of the founding members of the Promise Keepers Board of Directors, and a frequent speaker at PK events around the country. On October 4, 1997 in the Nation's Capitol, James delivered the Gospel message at *Stand in the Gap*—an event attended by 1.4 million men, and broadcast live to over 20 different nations around the world.

James and his wife, Belinda, have four grown children and currently live in Tennessee.

www.truthworks.org
1-800-597-4502

About Promise Keepers

Promise Keepers is a Christian outreach aimed at building men of integrity. Through arena conferences, ongoing local small groups, educational seminars, resource materials, and local churches, Promise Keepers encourages men to live godly lives and to keep seven basic promises of commitment to God, their families, and fellow men. Promise Keepers seeks to unite Christian men of all races, denominations, ages, cultures, and socio-economic groups, believing that accountable relationships among men are critical in helping one another become promise keepers in their relationships with God, their wives, their children, each other, and their communities.

HISTORY

On March 20, 1990, the head football coach for the University of Colorado, Bill McCartney, and his friend Dave Wardell, Ph.D., were on a three-hour car ride to a Fellowship of Christian Athletes (FCA) meeting, when they first discussed the idea of filling a stadium with Christian men. Later that year, 72 men began to fast and pray about the concept of thousands of men coming together for the purpose of Christian discipleship. In July 1991, 4,200 men gathered for the first Promise Keepers conference at the University of Colorado basketball arena. Since then, nearly five million men have attended more than 100 Promise Keepers stadium and arena conferences.

Mission

Promise Keepers Mission Statement is direct and succinct: Men Transformed Worldwide.

GLOBAL MINISTRIES

Promise Keepers has a growing international ministry with activity in more than 30 countries located on every continent. Events have been held in South Africa, Puerto Rico, Mexico, Costa Rica, Ghana, the Philippines, and other areas over the globe.

Meanwhile, Promise Keepers continues to receive inquiries about developing men's ministries from countries around the world. More than 100,000 men have attended men's events directly related to Promise Keepers in countries outside the United States.

LOCAL SMALL GROUPS

Across the country and around the world, hundreds of small groups of men have continued to gather on a regular basis for Bible studies and personal accountability. These local small groups of men are led independently of Promise Keepers, but many use Promise Keepers resources for study and encouragement.

RESOURCE MATERIALS

Promise Keepers also develops and provides numerous resources for personal study and men's groups. These resources include audio/video recordings, radio broadcasts, books, study guides, worship tapes, and apparel.

CONTACT

For more information on Promise Keepers, please call 1-800-888-7595 or visit our exciting website at www.promisekeepers.org.